CONTENTS

Published 2010. Pedigree Books Ltd, Beech Hill House, Walnut Gardens, Exeter, Devon EX4 4DH
books@pedigreegroup.co.uk | www.pedigreebooks.com
MARVEL, Super Hero Squad: TM & © 2010 Marvel Entertainment, Inc. and its subsidiaries.
Licensed by Marvel Characters B.V. www.marvel.com. All rights reserved.

Pedigree®

£7.99

When the Infinity Sword gets shattered, evil Dr Doom mounts a frantic mission to get it back. He's desperate to get his hands on every last fractile of the weapon, knowing that the sword is the single most powerful object in the Universe! Only one thing stands in Doom's way – Iron Man and his hotshot team of Super Heroes.

Iron Man's recruits are the best of the best. The might of legendary Thor is joined by the rage of Hulk and the glinting blades of Wolverine. The Squad's Helicarrier HQ becomes home to the toughest crack crew of heroes ever to fly over the city. Their days are spent fighting off Doom and his treachery, their nights are spent goofing around, snacking out and arguing over the remote control. Sure they don't always get along, but things are always interesting when the Super Hero Squad is in town!

TIME TO HERO UP!

IRON MAN

Iron Man's the leader and self-confessed gadget addict of the gang, a thinking Super Hero with attitude! He wears an ultra-tough plated bodysuit strong enough to repel enemy lasers, bombs and streaking bullets. Some of the tech-head's other inventions aren't quite as effective, blowing up before they've even got off the ground! None of this bugs Iron Man. He always looks on the bright side – even when the Squaddies' backs are up against the wall!

WOLVERINE

There's not many Squaddies rougher or tougher than Wolverine. The clawed crusader believes in swiping first and asking questions later! He's still got a lot to learn about teamwork, but when Doom's henchmen are on the offensive Wolvie will defend 'til the end. If he takes a knock, the hero uses his mutant healing powers to get right back at 'em! Off-duty it's a different story – Wolverine is a light-hearted prankster who can't help setting up his buddies time and time again.

HULK

Would you be nuts enough to mess with the green gamma guy? Hulk is a man mountain of pure muscle and the strongest Squaddie in the crew. Don't be fooled by his simple ways and child-like love of ice cream and 'toons – if this dude gets mad he'll punch doors and kick through bricks to get to his adversary. Hulk might be green and mean, but he's totally loyal to Iron Man and the rest of his friends. If there's a villain on the attack, he'll block them at every turn.

GENERAL 'THUNDERBOLT ROSS'

It's not easy keeping the Super Hero Squad in order – personalities this strong don't like being told what to do! It's no wonder then that the General is in a bad mood 99% of the time. The grumpy veteran deserves his fair share of respect, Ross is a decorated soldier and a top strategist when it comes to psyching out and defeating the enemy. Taking on Doom doesn't phase him one bit, he knows that getting his wayward heroes to listen up will prove a much bigger challenge!

THOR

This blonde bombshell is a legend in his own mind! Thor is on loan to Super Hero City from the fabled kingdom of Asgard, a mighty warrior with an all-powerful hammer called Mjolnir. The magical weapon possesses the ability to control the weather and open portals to other dimensions! When Thor's not fighting alongside Iron Man, you'll catch him proclaiming oaths of admiration to the nearest mirror. As far as his heroic good looks go, Thor can't help being enchanted!

SILVER SURFER

Even when there are Sentinels posted at every exit and chaos rampaging through the skies, the Surfer won't panic. He's a chilled out sky-rider bestowed with cosmic powers – a few strikes from Doom and his cronies ain't gonna ruffle this dude's feathers one bit! Silver Surfer gets his kicks from hurtling around at jaw-dropping speeds. Back at HQ, the Super-Squaddie practices awesome new moves on his mirror board.

GET READY TO MEET THE SQUADDIES...

TIME TO HERO UP!

SPIDER-MAN

Spidey has got his hands full battling crime in his own city, but the good-hearted web-slinger is always ready to swing in and help out when the Squad need some extra fighting power. Spider-Man is equipped with an impressive list of hero powers and a unique sixth sense that allows him to sense danger from miles around. When he's not shooting webs or running up the side of buildings, Spidey is making the crew laugh with a volley of daft wisecracks and silly jokes.

FALCON

Even though he's a hotshot soldier and a flying expert, Falcon is still a rookie on the Super Hero team. The youngster has got lots to prove, but his awesome aerial prowess is already making him indispensable. Falcon wears a special winged harness made out of a solid hologram called 'Hard Light'. It gives him the ability to soar through the clouds, dive-bombing baddies at tremendous speeds. Falcon uses his mind to communicate with birds, and has an especially close relationship with his pet falcon Redwing.

CYCLOPS

Cyclops pulverises villains with his powerful optic energy beams, burning rays that can rupture steel plates and turn rock into rubble. When this guy reports in for duty, he gives 110% – following his brief to the letter. Some may say that Cykes' love of the rules makes him a spoilsport, but the hero has saved the day many times just by keeping his wayward buddies focused and on-task. The visor-clad hero will do anything to see off evil, working out brilliant battle plans or mounting fearsome martial arts attacks.

INVISIBLE WOMAN

Only Invisible Woman has the power to make the entire Super Hero Squad disappear! She can make anyone and anything totally transparent at the blink of an eye, summoning force fields that protect the Squaddies' from Dr Doom's ruthless attacks. Iron Man and the gang make sure that Invisible Woman is invited on every mission. It's not just because she's a top hero – they know the feisty firecracker will make them vanish if she gets left out!

ICEMAN

Cool dude Iceman is still new to the Super Hero Squad and he loves every icy minute. He's admired the heroes all his life and is totally over-excited about working side-by-side with Hulk, Wolverine and the rest of the crew. The chilly mutant has got lots to learn about the true responsibility of being a Squaddie, but Iceman's blasts of Arctic cold always come in handy when it's time to put some villains on ice.

NICK FURY

Nick formed the Super Hero Squad when his espionage agency S.H.I.E.L.D struggled to cope with the onslaught of evil from Doom and his minions. The eye-patched superspy had government authority to scour the city for crimefighters, building the toughest crack Super Hero team in the world. Nick has an impressive military track record and top knowledge of weapons and fighting techniques. He knows just when to send the Squaddies in, guiding the elite force to victory every time.

GET READY TO
MEET THE SQUADDIES...

TIME TO HERO UP!

THING

The thundering form of Thing is enough to send even the bulkiest baddie running for cover! When it's clobbering time, the blue-eyed Squaddie will batter through walls and blast through concrete to get to the source of the trouble. Thing can be touchy at times, but the heroes understand that it's only because his revoltin' rock-covered body isn't the easiest mutation to live with. Thing always cheers up when there's a meal on the menu – munching his way through super-sized snacks and treats.

HUMAN TORCH

Human Torch is Invisible Woman's brash kid brother, an enthusiastic youngster who is still learning how to play with fire. His impressive abilities allow him to flame up anytime and anywhere, controlling the temperatures around him. Torch has got a terrible temper, blasting opponents as he rages through the city sky. Although he's hot to handle, all the Squaddies agree that he's one of the most powerful and trustworthy members of the crew.

MR FANTASTIC

This stretchy Squaddie isn't just super-strong, he's super-smart too! Mr Fantastic is one of the top brains behind the Marvel Super Hero Squad, a genius with a taste for scientific mysteries. He has a strong moral duty to defend right and triumph over evil, but stretching his pliable elastic body doesn't excite him any more. Mr F would much rather be studying charts back at HQ, using his superior brain power to work out ways of tying Doom's Sentinels in knots.

REPTIL

Reptil is new to the Super Hero Squad – a kid with lots of potential and even more to learn. He can be hot-headed and hard to control, but he's slowly working out what it means to 'Hero Up'. Reptil draws his energy from a unique prehistoric sunstone. When he clutches the rock he can channel all kinds of knockout dinosaur abilities. Whether its Pterodactyl wings or Velociraptor legs, Reptil is totally unstoppable in dino form!

COLOSSUS

Colossus is a giant amongst the citizens of Super Hero City. The imposing powerhouse is able to transform his body into impenetrable 'organic steel' – making him a titan of stamina and strength. Colossus is virtually indestructible, weapons simply glancing off his rock-hard frame. The mild-mannered mutant is also a creative whiz, sketching out awesome comic strips of the Squad's adventures. The gang love reading his strips and checking out their own cool hero portraits!

HAWKEYE

The archer known as Hawkeye was recruited for his nerves of steel and determination to cast evil out of the city. The hero's arrows can hit a target from eye-popping distances and his repertoire of trick shots never fails to stun and amaze his friends. As well as being a top marksman, Hawkeye is an acrobatic gymnast with a taste for danger. As soon as one villain is sent packing, he's cooking up a scheme for the next adventure – the more perilous the better.

GET READY TO
MEET THE SQUADDIES...

VILLAINS FIGHT BACK!

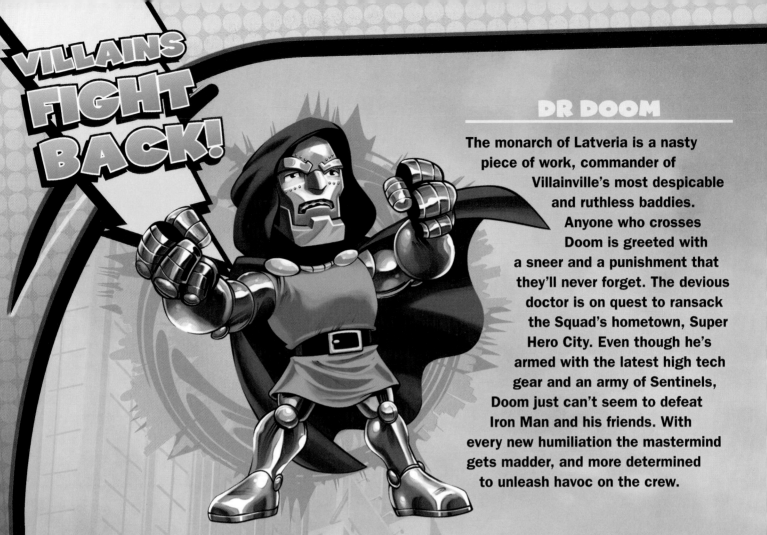

DR DOOM

The monarch of Latveria is a nasty piece of work, commander of Villainville's most despicable and ruthless baddies. Anyone who crosses Doom is greeted with a sneer and a punishment that they'll never forget. The devious doctor is on quest to ransack the Squad's hometown, Super Hero City. Even though he's armed with the latest high tech gear and an army of Sentinels, Doom just can't seem to defeat Iron Man and his friends. With every new humiliation the mastermind gets madder, and more determined to unleash havoc on the crew.

MAGNETO

Doom's second-in-command is a power-hungry mutant who storms through his days in a permanent bad mood. He's a fearsome rival for the Squaddies – the villain's extraordinary magnetism enables him to break up metal and seize weapons from his enemies. The downside is that office equipment, nails and kitchen utensils also end up getting attracted to Magneto's face! Magneto is often sent on expeditions with Abomination.

ABOMINATION

Abomination cuts a terrifying figure as he plunders through the city streets, bashing anyone and anything that stands in his path. The super-baddy was mutated from the same gamma rays that created Hulk, but he chose deviousness over decency and honour. Abomination uses gills to breathe underwater and his 900-pound body is covered with slimy green scales. Many are repulsed, but only the foolish dare admit it to his face – as far as Abomination is concerned, he's the best-looking baddie in Villainville!

SUPER SKRULL

This lethal agent started out as a shape-shifting intergalactic soldier, but everything changed when he got biologically enhanced by the Skrull Emperor. Now Super Skrull boasts all the superpowers of the Fantastic Four! He combines Mr Fantastic's elasticity with Invisible Woman's force fields, Human Torch's flame-throwing and Thing's impenetrable skin! The Super Hero Squad are constantly battling the powerful pest and trying out new strategies to keep his bad behaviour in check.

THERE'S SOME VILE
VILLAINS LURKING OUT THERE...

15

VILLAINS FIGHT BACK!

LOKI

Thor's shamed half-brother is hell-bent on wreaking mischief on a massive scale! Loki has become infamous in Super Hero City, a malevolent sorcerer who delights in tormenting his Asgardian brother and rival crew. He should never be under-estimated, Loki's powers of magic and misdirection can cause great harm to those he casts under his spell. The Norse God of Bad Stuff, Loki has extra-sensory abilities and the power to harness energy for his own villainous purposes.

MYSTIQUE

This blue-skinned trickster is no lady – Mystique gets what she wants by using stealth and deception. Sly from her head down to her toes, she is able to change shape and form to flawlessly impersonate any person or hero she chooses. Even though Mystique is not a super-strong fighter, her intellect outstrips both Magneto and Doom. She believes that the best way to oust Iron Man and his friends is to catch the Squad when they're off-guard.

DOC OCK

Dr Octopus is a highly gifted, but hopelessly insane scientist who wants to rule the world! The Doc constantly plots to control both the heroes and the villains of Super Hero City. He's not alone in this quest – the twisted genius has created four robotic arms to help him. Each cybernetic tentacle obeys Doc Ock's mental commands, extending far beyond the length of his body. With his bionic body parts, the Doctor can climb up buildings and duel with the fiercest of rivals.

THE SENTINELS

When Dr Doom set out to destroy Super Hero City, he built a robot army to do his dirty work for him. The result was the Sentinels. Each Sentinel is several storeys high, possessing the capability to stride through the streets or fly at super-human speeds. Resisting the devious droids is a full-time job for the Squad. Each robot is fitted with heat-resistant armour and retractable capture cables that it shoots out to grab its prey.

THERE'S SOME VILE
VILLAINS LURKING OUT THERE...

THOR'S WORD CRUSH

Thor has lost his mythical hammer! Not only does the weapon wield great force, it's the must-have accessory for the thunder god's Super Hero outfit! Help get it back by working out the mighty mallet's true name.

Smashing through this word puzzle is easy! Crack the clues then read the name that appears in the vertical yellow boxes.

1. Who is the leader of the Super Hero Squad?
2. What transportation devices are fitted to the Sentinels' feet?
3. What is the name of Thor's pesky half-brother?
4. Where does Dr Doom and his cronies live?
5. What good guy has a super-stretchy body?
6. Which government agency assigned Hawkeye to the Squad?
7. What defence mechanism is Invisible Woman able to generate?

CALLING ALL SQUADDIES!

Have you got the brain of a Super Hero? Put your observation skills to the test! Study this picture for 30 seconds, fixing every detail in your mind. Then turn over the page and answer as many questions as you can.

COME ON SQUAD, IT'S TIME TO HERO UP!

EMERGENCY! THE SQUAD HAS TO CHECK OUT A DISTURBANCE IN SUPER HERO CITY! I'M LOOKING FOR AN EXTRA HERO TO TAKE ON THIS MISSION. ARE YOU UP FOR THE JOB?

CALLING ALL SQUADDIES!

1. **WHERE ARE THE SQUADDIES?**

   _____

2. **WHO IS SLIDING DOWN THE EMERGENCY POLE?**

   _____

3. **HOW MANY SCREENS SHOWING THE GENERAL DID YOU SPOT?**

   _____

4. **WHICH HERO IS HANGING FROM THE CEILING?**

   _____

5. **WHAT IS MR FANTASTIC DOING?**

   _____

6. **HOW MANY SQUADDIES ARE THERE IN TOTAL?**

   _____

Ready to take the test? Give yourself three minutes to answer all the questions above. Make sure you focus – the Thunderbolt is watching!

CYBER COPY

USE THIS GRID TO HELP YOU DRAW A COOL PICTURE OF DOC OCK AND HIS COILING CYBERNETIC ARMS. USE A PENCIL TO COPY EACH SQUARE OF THE BADDIE FROM THE LITTLE GRID INTO THE BIG ONE BELOW. NOW COLOUR HIM IN!

REPTIL JOINS FORCES

PART ONE

REPTIL FELT HIS SUNSTONE BLAZE RUBY RED.

"'Raptor claws!" he yelled, lunging towards Wolverine. The Hero's hands instantly morphed into the razor-sharp talons of a prehistoric dinosaur.

Quick as a flash Wolverine blocked the rookie with his own steel talons.

"Trying to play me at my own game, are you?" he grinned. "I like it!"

The friends had being practising their hero stances for hours now, but neither wanted to be the first to give up. Reptil was the Super Hero Squad's newest recruit and Wolvie had been assigned as his trainer. Their workouts were always tough.

"Time to cool it guys," said Iron Man, walking into the Helicarrier's combat chamber. "You could both do with a break."

REPTIL JOINS FORCES

PART ONE

REPTIL shook his head, hoping the others wouldn't notice how out of puff he'd got.

"Did my dinopowers tire ya out?" he cried, prodding Wolverine in the ribs.

The trainer pushed past the youngster, then gulped down a drink from the water cooler.

"Can't take no more?" grinned Reptil. "I can keep jabbing all night!"

Underneath his mask Iron Man raised his eyes – if Reptil thought he could outdo a Hero like Wolverine, he still had a lot to learn.

"What a Reptwerp!" muttered the clawed crusader, brushing him aside with an effortless shove. "Being a Super Hero is about so much more than wielding powers. It's about honour and teamwork."

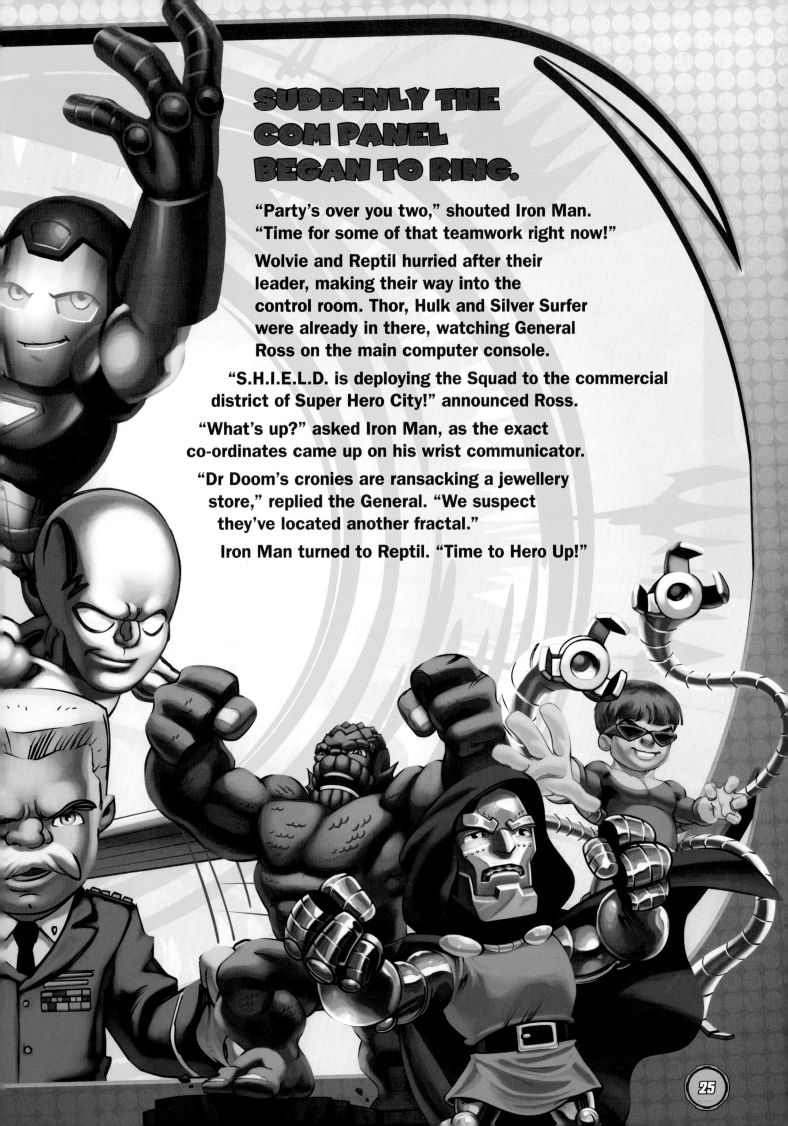

SUDDENLY THE COM PANEL BEGAN TO RING.

"Party's over you two," shouted Iron Man. "Time for some of that teamwork right now!"

Wolvie and Reptil hurried after their leader, making their way into the control room. Thor, Hulk and Silver Surfer were already in there, watching General Ross on the main computer console.

"S.H.I.E.L.D. is deploying the Squad to the commercial district of Super Hero City!" announced Ross.

"What's up?" asked Iron Man, as the exact co-ordinates came up on his wrist communicator.

"Dr Doom's cronies are ransacking a jewellery store," replied the General. "We suspect they've located another fractal."

Iron Man turned to Reptil. "Time to Hero Up!"

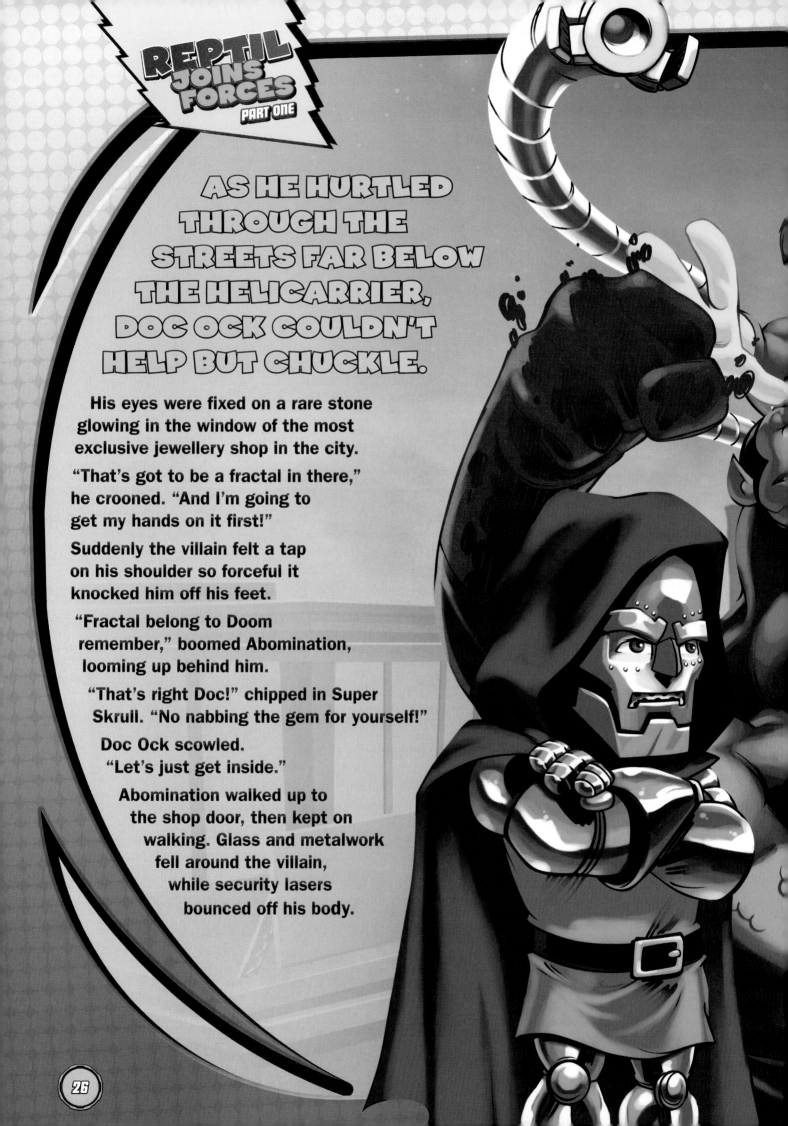

REPTIL JOINS FORCES
PART ONE

AS HE HURTLED THROUGH THE STREETS FAR BELOW THE HELICARRIER, DOC OCK COULDN'T HELP BUT CHUCKLE.

His eyes were fixed on a rare stone glowing in the window of the most exclusive jewellery shop in the city.

"That's got to be a fractal in there," he crooned. "And I'm going to get my hands on it first!"

Suddenly the villain felt a tap on his shoulder so forceful it knocked him off his feet.

"Fractal belong to Doom remember," boomed Abomination, looming up behind him.

"That's right Doc!" chipped in Super Skrull. "No nabbing the gem for yourself!"

Doc Ock scowled. "Let's just get inside."

Abomination walked up to the shop door, then kept on walking. Glass and metalwork fell around the villain, while security lasers bounced off his body.

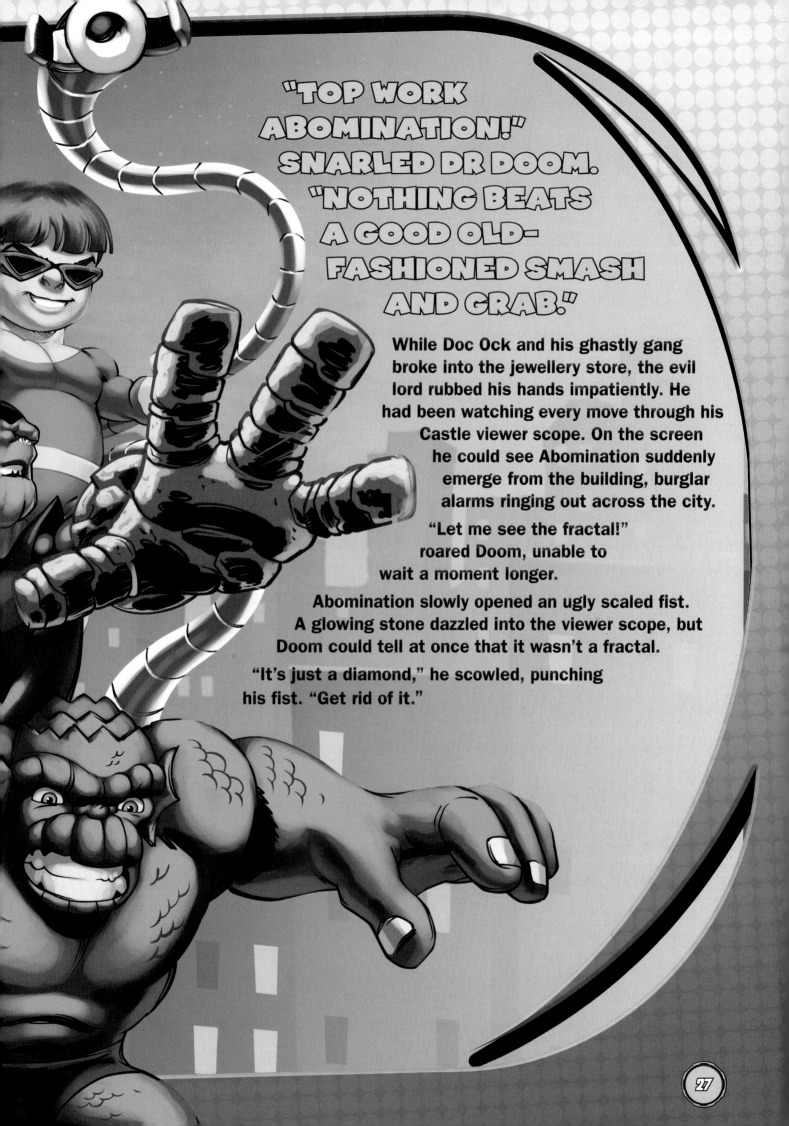

"TOP WORK ABOMINATION!" SNARLED DR DOOM. "NOTHING BEATS A GOOD OLD-FASHIONED SMASH AND GRAB."

While Doc Ock and his ghastly gang broke into the jewellery store, the evil lord rubbed his hands impatiently. He had been watching every move through his Castle viewer scope. On the screen he could see Abomination suddenly emerge from the building, burglar alarms ringing out across the city.

"Let me see the fractal!" roared Doom, unable to wait a moment longer.

Abomination slowly opened an ugly scaled fist. A glowing stone dazzled into the viewer scope, but Doom could tell at once that it wasn't a fractal.

"It's just a diamond," he scowled, punching his fist. "Get rid of it."

REPTIL JOINS FORCES
PART ONE

ABOMINATION HURLED THE DIAMOND TOWARDS THE GUTTER.

Before the gem could clatter onto the sidewalk, a dazzling light blinded the evil gang. Doc Ock and the other degenerates covered their eyes as the Silver Surfer's shiny mirror board glided to a stop in front of them.

"Greetings!" smiled the Sentinel of the Spaceways, "Are we all having a brilliant time?"

Iron Man, Wolverine and Thor appeared behind him, each grabbing a villain by the arm. Reptil dropped to the pavement too, his heart pounding with excitement.

"Find that diamond," ordered Iron Man, pointing towards the gutter.

Reptil grasped his sunstone, then instantly developed Pterodactyl vision.

"There it is!" he yelled, locating the gem in seconds.

While the other Squaddies held the baddies at bay, the rookie returned the diamond to its display case.

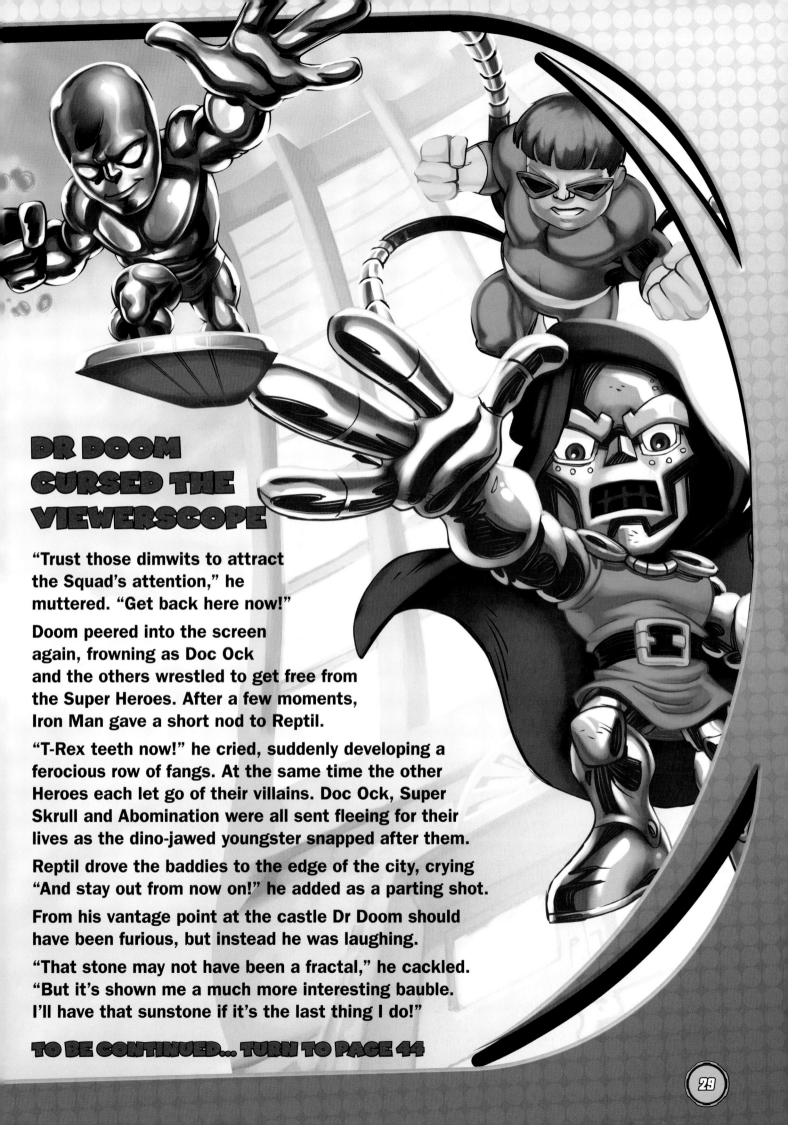

DR DOOM CURSED THE VIEWERSCOPE

"Trust those dimwits to attract the Squad's attention," he muttered. "Get back here now!"

Doom peered into the screen again, frowning as Doc Ock and the others wrestled to get free from the Super Heroes. After a few moments, Iron Man gave a short nod to Reptil.

"T-Rex teeth now!" he cried, suddenly developing a ferocious row of fangs. At the same time the other Heroes each let go of their villains. Doc Ock, Super Skrull and Abomination were all sent fleeing for their lives as the dino-jawed youngster snapped after them.

Reptil drove the baddies to the edge of the city, crying "And stay out from now on!" he added as a parting shot.

From his vantage point at the castle Dr Doom should have been furious, but instead he was laughing.

"That stone may not have been a fractal," he cackled. "But it's shown me a much more interesting bauble. I'll have that sunstone if it's the last thing I do!"

TO BE CONTINUED... TURN TO PAGE 44

CREATE YOUR OWN COMIC STRIP

COLOSSUS IS A WHIZ WHEN IT COMES TO COMIC STRIPS! AFTER A HARD DAY'S HEROING, THE SQUADDIE'S SKETCHING SKILLS KEEP THE GANG AMUSED FOR HOURS ON END. HERE'S YOUR CHANCE TO DRAW A BRAND NEW ADVENTURE FOR COLOSSUS AND HIS PALS.

Colossus has started the story for you. Can you finish it off? Draw in the characters and then add captions, speech bubbles and knock-out sound effects! Don't forget to sketch yourself into the action too.

Wolvie, Iron Man and Thor were paying a visit to _____ 's school.

RUSH & RESCUE

THERE'S A MAN-EATING MONSTER RAMPAGING THROUGH THE CITY! FALCON, SPIDEY AND THE SILVER SURFER HAVE ALL BEEN SUMMONED BY GENERAL ROSS, BUT WHO CAN GET THERE FASTEST? FOLLOW THE SWOOSHES OF LIGHT TO FIND OUT WHO'S GONNA BE FIRST AT THE SCENE!

A) FALCON

B) SPIDER-MAN

C) SILVER SURFER

DR DOOM'S HIT LIST

DR DOOM IS SICK OF BEING DEFEATED BY THE SUPER HEROES!
HE'S SUMMONED HIS VILEST VILLAINS TO AN URGENT BRIEFING AT THE CASTLE.
THEIR MISSION? TO TRACK DOWN AND CAPTURE HIS FIVE MOST-HATED
ENEMIES! READ DOOM'S DESCRIPTIONS, THEN GUESS WHO'S ON THE HIT LIST.

1. Leader of the Super Hero Squad. Obsessed with technology. Targets us with all manner of pesky new gadgets. *The Super Hero is...*

2. Transformed by gamma rays. A giant of a hero with strength to match. Super-aggressive when angry. *The Super Hero is...*

3. Throws flames of intense heat. Lights up the night sky. Invisible Woman's headstrong little brother. *The Super Hero is...*

4. An enemy of all things evil. Attacks with a bow and arrow. An ace athlete who's always on-duty. *The Super Hero is...*

5. A towering lump of walking rock who can be a bit touchy at times. But give him some pizza and he'll be your friend for life. *The Super Hero is...*

DOT-TO-DOT DUEL

HUMAN TORCH

Whenever he sees Skrull, Human Torch gets all fired up! The junior fireball is the hottest thing in Super Hero City – bar none.

INVISIBLE WOMAN

The strength of her force fields are like an iron wall – tough enough to repel Skrull's fiercest attacks!

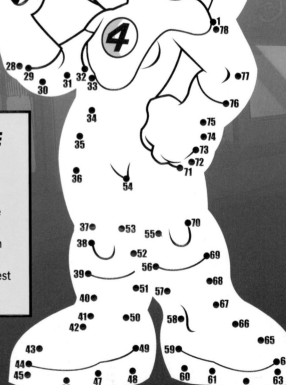

When Super Skrull gets nasty, it's time to send in the Fantastic Four! This awesome foursome have the abilities to match Skrull's superpowers and send the vile villain packing.

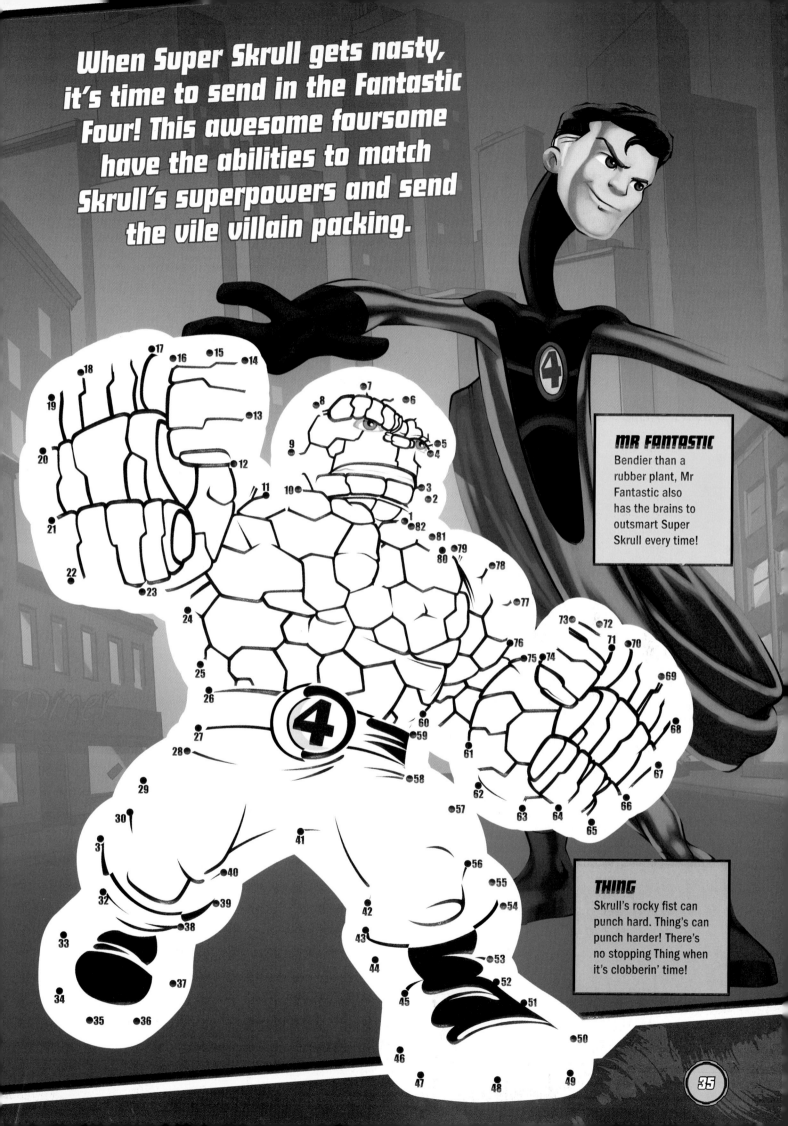

MR FANTASTIC
Bendier than a rubber plant, Mr Fantastic also has the brains to outsmart Super Skrull every time!

THING
Skrull's rocky fist can punch hard. Thing's can punch harder! There's no stopping Thing when it's clobberin' time!

WHO SAID THAT?

Both the Super Hero Squad and their enemies are outspoken bunches! Can you work out who's been mouthing off this time around? Study the speech bubbles and then match each saying to the right hero or villain.

A) MAGNETO

B) WOLVERINE

C) REPTIL

1 'HAVE AT THEE, VILE DOG!'

2 'I AM THE MASTER OF MAGNETISM!'

3 'LET'S MAKE SOME MISCHIEF'

4 'SPACE OUT AND SURF UP!'

5 'BACK OFF, BUB!'

6 'MY POWERS ARE DINO-MITE!'

D) THOR

E) LOKI

F) SILVER SURFER

BULK UP HULK

When the gamma guy's tummy starts to rumble, he needs to chow down fast! Hulk's favourite super-quick snack is a bowl of this sweet, sticky popcorn. He'll bash through walls to get himself some! Why not whip up a batch to share with your own super-hungry pals?

FOR ONE BATCH, YOU WILL NEED:

- 500g bag of popping corn
- 150g butter
- 150g light muscovado sugar
- 180g mini marshmallows
- 3 packets of milk chocolate buttons

HOT CORN CAN BURN! DON'T TRY THIS RECIPE WITHOUT ASKING AN ADULT TO HELP.

Hungry Hulk Popcorn

1. Pour 60g of the popping corn into a plastic bowl with a lid and then ask an adult to microwave it for you for 2 ½ - 3 minutes. You'll hear lots of bangs as the little kernels explode into yummy popcorn.

2. Tip the popcorn into a large bowl then repeat step 1 until there's plenty for all your friends.

3. Pour the butter and sugar into a saucepan and stir until it melts. The ingredients will quickly dissolve into a sticky caramel sauce.

4. Drizzle the caramel over the bowl of popcorn.

5. While the caramel is still warm, fold in the marshmallows and chocolate buttons. Give the popcorn a good stir to make sure the sticky mixture is evenly spread.

6. Spoon the Hulk popcorn into plastic cups then pass them round to all your friends!

NOW'S THE TIME TO SNACK OUT AND RELAX IN FRONT OF YOUR FAVOURITE EPISODE OF THE SUPER HERO SQUAD SHOW!

LIGHT 'EM UP!

Those vile villains have crept into Super Hero City under the cover of darkness! There are eight baddies roaming the sleeping streets – locating all eight is Human Torch's number one priority! Shed some light on the search by naming each of the suspiciously villain-shaped shadows.

1. _____ _____

2. _____

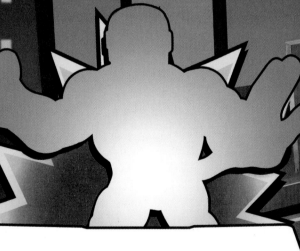

3. _____

4. _____

5. _____

6. _____ _____

7. ___ _____

8. _____

STILL STRUGGLING TO WORK OUT WHO'S WHO? USE THIS NAME BOARD TO HELP YOU.

ABOMINATION.............. ☐
SENTINEL..................... ☐
DR DOOM .... ☐
MAGNETO .... ☐
LOKI............................... ☐
SUPER SKRULL .... ☐
MYSTIQUE .... ☐
DOC OCK .... ☐

DISAPPEARING LETTERS

THE SQUADDIES NEVER CROSS INVISIBLE WOMAN – WITH A FLICK OF THE WRIST SHE COULD MAKE EACH AND EVERY ONE OF THEM DISAPPEAR INTO THIN AIR! WHEN SHE GETS MAD THIS LADY ALWAYS GETS EVEN. IF IT'S NOT BY USING HER SUPERPOWERS, IT'S PLAYING JOKES ON HER PALS.

G	P	D	G	O	H	Z	H	P	K
W	I	V	Q	K	P	B	S	N	X
B	J	F	K	E	X	K	K	S	V
X	J	Y	V	D	Z	U	L	F	H
H	K	C	W	Q	P	A	R	P	W
R	Q	Y	U	R	O	G	L	D	U
Q	L	H	X	H	Y	D	V	Z	V
K	Y	J	X	M	H	F	O	J	B
P	D	P	K	D	Q	D	G	L	K
V	Z	O	H	P	W	J	F	Y	Q

Invisible Woman has hidden the identity of another prankster in this word box. Cross out all the letters that appear more than once, then rearrange the ones left over to spell out his name.

THE SUPER HERO IS

___ ___ ___ ___ ___ ___

MORPHING MYSTIQUE

Mystique is a master of disguise, morphing her form to confuse her enemies. The Super Hero Squad has cornered the sly enchantress in a disused warehouse, but she's up to her old tricks again!

STUDY THE DATA PROFILE OF MYSTIQUE, THEN CIRCLE THE PICTURE THAT MATCHES IT EXACTLY.

NAME:
MYSTIQUE

SUPER SKILLS:
EXTREME AGILITY,
SHAPE-SHIFTING,
HEALING POWERS

CATCHPHRASE:
'RESIST ME AT YOUR PERIL!'

A

B

C

D

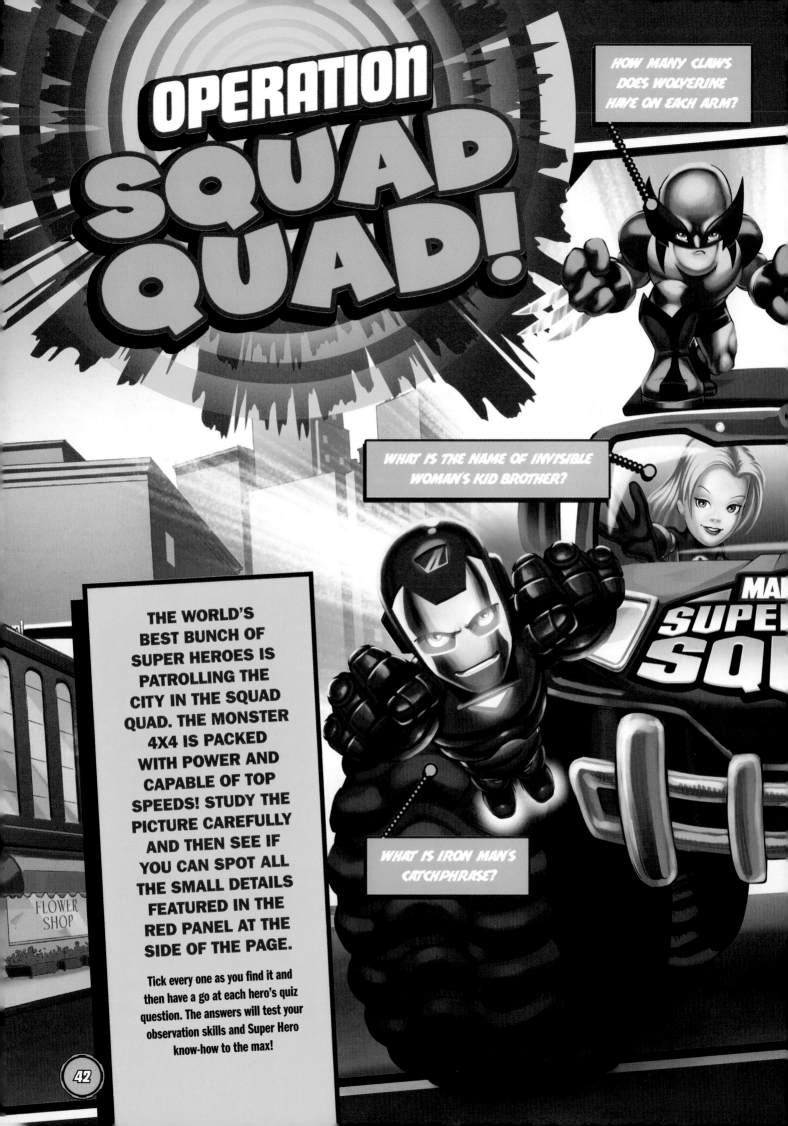

REPTIL JOINS FORCES PART TWO

REPTIL took a seat in the Helicarrier's debrief room, still feeling pumped from the showdown with Doom's degenerates. Wolverine strolled in, giving his student a high five as he passed.

"Good team work back there," he called, taking a seat next to Thor. "Maybe you are learning something after all!"

The Norse God pointed his mighty hammer at Reptil, then flashed him a gleaming white grin. "'Odin himself would applaud thee!"

"Thanks guys," said the youngster, jumping to his feet. "I'm gonna go back out and check those losers haven't slunk back into town."

"Thing and Hulk are on it already," said Iron Man. "You've played your part today."

Reptil's face fell. "But I can do it!"

Iron Man shook his head. "You did well, but now it's time for the big guys to get involved. Go get some rest."

REPTIL STARED SULKILY OUT OF HIS BEDROOM WINDOW

The Helicarrier was gliding silently through the afternoon sky, high above the streets of Super Hero City.

"Hulk and Thing are getting some action down there," he muttered to himself. "I want some too!"

Suddenly there was a knock at the window. The Squaddie leapt to his feet and peered through the reinforced glass.

"Mystique!" he gasped, rubbing his eyesin disbelief. "What's a lowlife like you doing up here?"

The blue-skinned shape-shifter was perched gracefully on the Helicarrier's wing, red hair trailing behind her.

"Dr Doom was impressed by your little dinosaur routine," she smirked. "Now he wants to offer you another challenge."

Reptil scowled. With evil this close he knew he should sound the Squad alarm, but something was holding him back.

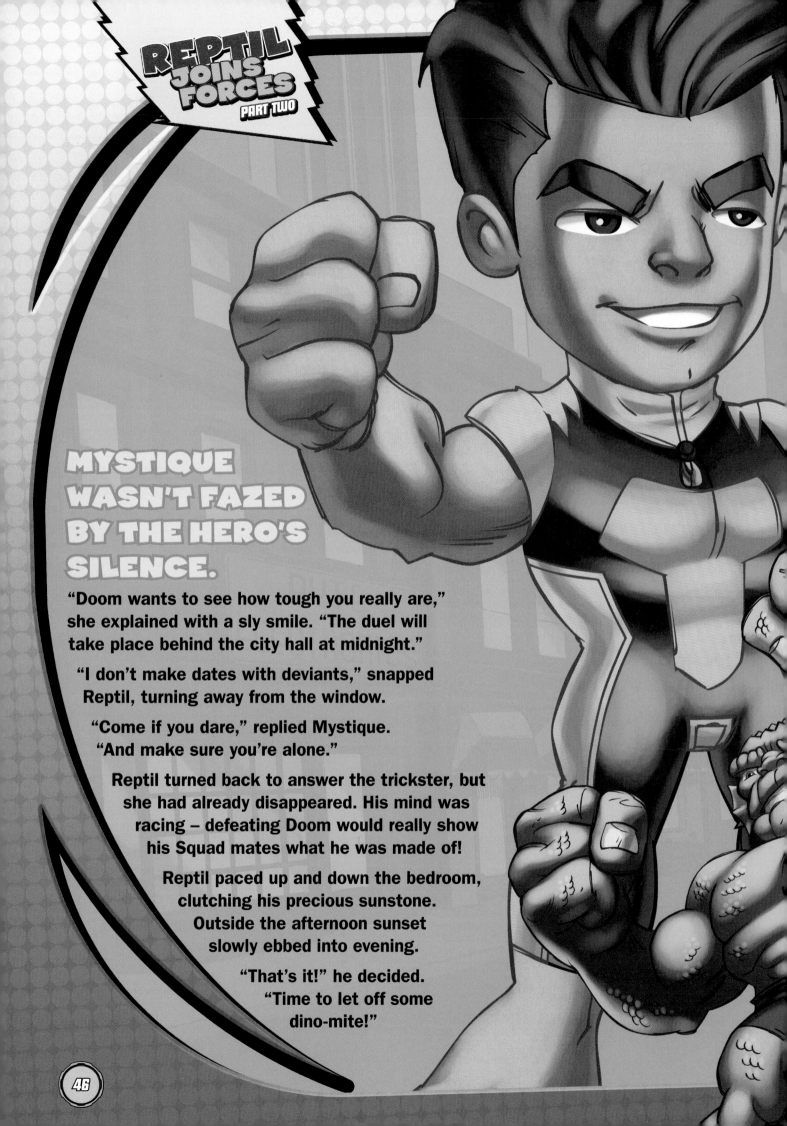

REPTIL JOINS FORCES
PART TWO

MYSTIQUE WASN'T FAZED BY THE HERO'S SILENCE.

"Doom wants to see how tough you really are," she explained with a sly smile. "The duel will take place behind the city hall at midnight."

"I don't make dates with deviants," snapped Reptil, turning away from the window.

"Come if you dare," replied Mystique. "And make sure you're alone."

Reptil turned back to answer the trickster, but she had already disappeared. His mind was racing – defeating Doom would really show his Squad mates what he was made of!

Reptil paced up and down the bedroom, clutching his precious sunstone. Outside the afternoon sunset slowly ebbed into evening.

"That's it!" he decided. "Time to let off some dino-mite!"

REPTIL'S HANDS SHOOK AS HE SPED ALONG THE DARK CITY STREETS.

Slipping out of the Helicarrier unnoticed had been tricky enough, but the main test was still to come. Within minutes the rookie had turned into an alley that skirted round the back of the city hall.

"Evening lizard-boy!" whispered Doom, stepping out of the shadows. "Are you ready?"

Reptil tried to look brave. "As I'll ever be!"

"Prepare to meet your doom!" screeched the evil doctor.

Suddenly Abomination, Doc Ock and Super Skrull thundered into the alley.

"This isn't a duel!" shouted Reptil. "You said one-on-one."

Doom sniggered. "Oops! I think I cheated!"

"Payback time!" boomed Abomination, as the villains moved in for the attack.

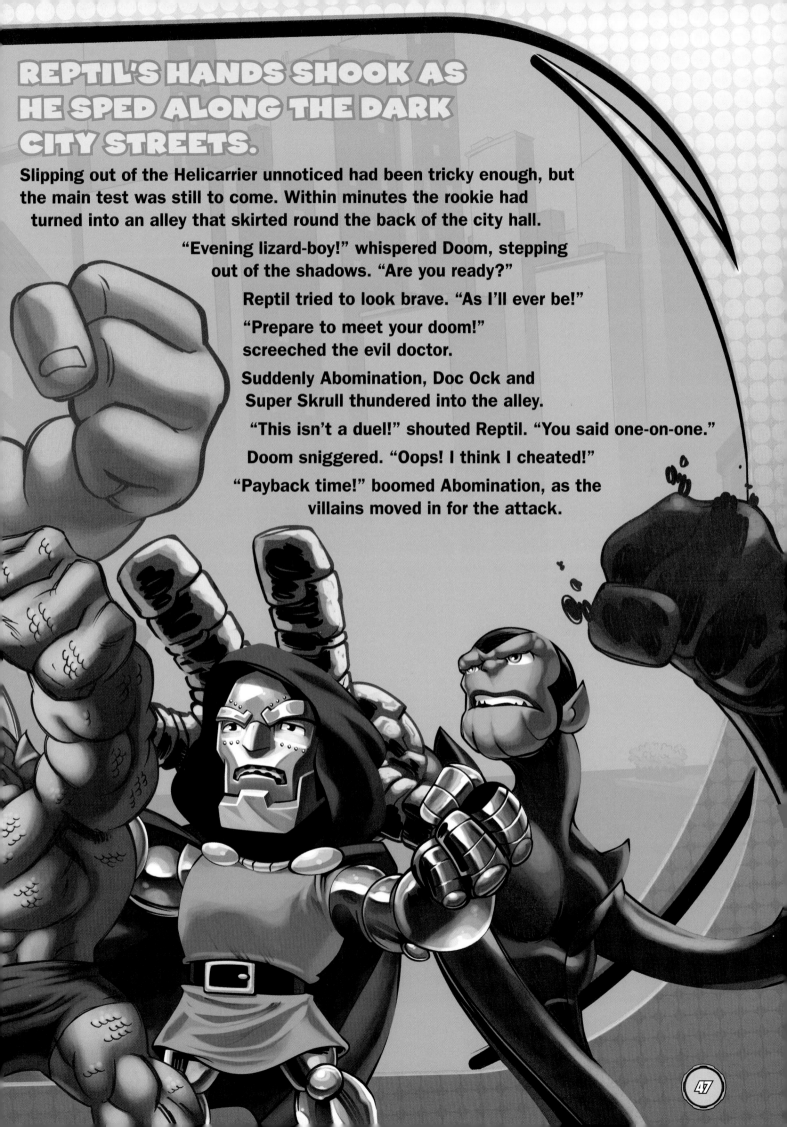

REPTIL JOINS FORCES PART TWO

"RAPTOR LEGS!" BELLOWED REPTIL, REACHING FOR HIS SUNSTONE.

Nothing happened. What was going on?

Doom threw his head back and laughed.

"Are you after this perhaps?" he asked, dangling the scarlet gem from his metal gauntlet.

Reptil started to panic. Doom's crew must have snatched the stone from him in the heat of the rumble!

"Give that back now, worm!" he shouted, reaching for the necklace.

In an instant Super Skrull bent his purple body round Doom, then used his rocky fist to lift the Squaddie clean into the air.

"Uh-uh!" he tutted. "The sunstone belongs to us now!"

"Playing dinosaurs is going to be sooo much fun!" added Doc Ock with a malicious grin.

"OH GOODY!" ECHOED A VOICE IN THE DARKNESS. "I LOVE PLAYTIME!"

Reptil looked up just as Wolverine leapt into view. Iron Man was right behind him, his eyes blazing with fury.

Doom and his henchmen groaned in disbelief.

"Keep away!" shouted the dark lord. "This is between me and Reptil!"

Iron Man forced the villains back to the wall with a blast of his repulsor rays.

"I don't think so Doom," he answered. "Us Squaddies come as a package."

There was a satisfying rip as Wolvie tore the sunstone from Doom's grasp. In a trice the Hero had retrieved the necklace and tossed it across to Reptil. "Time to Hero Up perhaps?" he grinned.

49

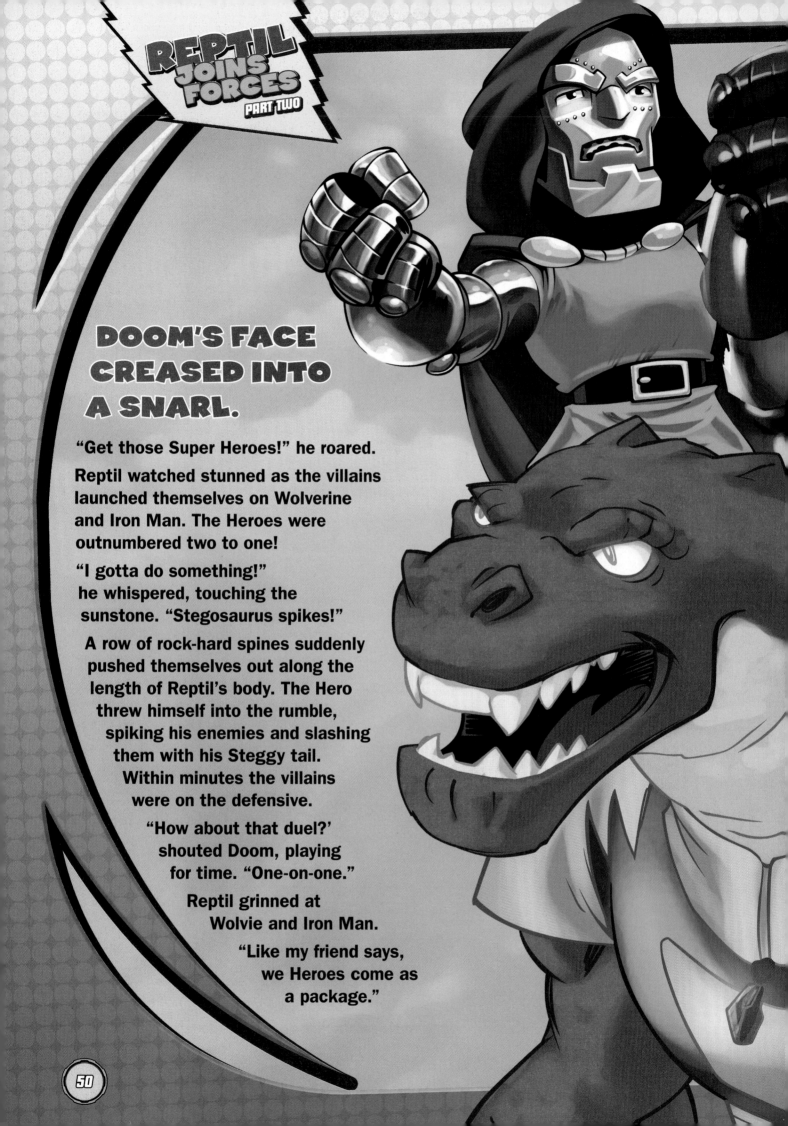

REPTIL JOINS FORCES
PART TWO

DOOM'S FACE CREASED INTO A SNARL.

"Get those Super Heroes!" he roared.

Reptil watched stunned as the villains launched themselves on Wolverine and Iron Man. The Heroes were outnumbered two to one!

"I gotta do something!" he whispered, touching the sunstone. "Stegosaurus spikes!"

A row of rock-hard spines suddenly pushed themselves out along the length of Reptil's body. The Hero threw himself into the rumble, spiking his enemies and slashing them with his Steggy tail. Within minutes the villains were on the defensive.

"How about that duel?' shouted Doom, playing for time. "One-on-one."

Reptil grinned at Wolvie and Iron Man.

"Like my friend says, we Heroes come as a package."

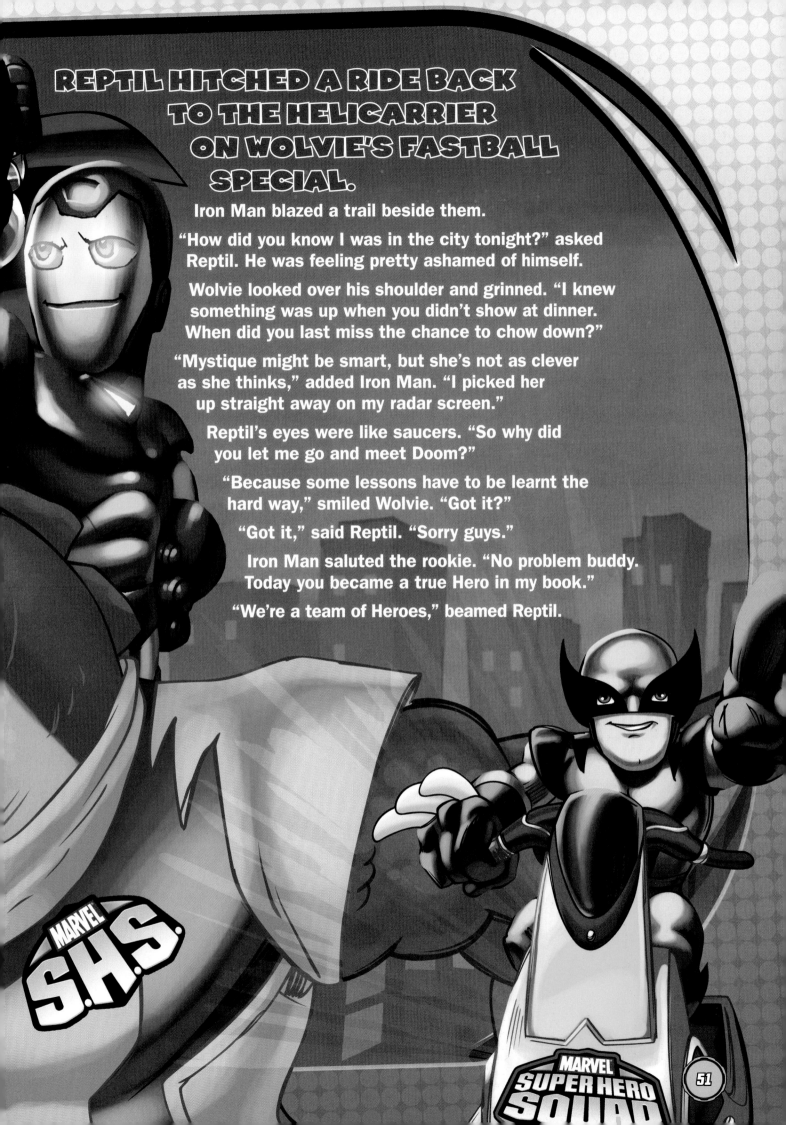

REPTIL HITCHED A RIDE BACK TO THE HELICARRIER ON WOLVIE'S FASTBALL SPECIAL.

Iron Man blazed a trail beside them.

"How did you know I was in the city tonight?" asked Reptil. He was feeling pretty ashamed of himself.

Wolvie looked over his shoulder and grinned. "I knew something was up when you didn't show at dinner. When did you last miss the chance to chow down?"

"Mystique might be smart, but she's not as clever as she thinks," added Iron Man. "I picked her up straight away on my radar screen."

Reptil's eyes were like saucers. "So why did you let me go and meet Doom?"

"Because some lessons have to be learnt the hard way," smiled Wolvie. "Got it?"

"Got it," said Reptil. "Sorry guys."

Iron Man saluted the rookie. "No problem buddy. Today you became a true Hero in my book."

"We're a team of Heroes," beamed Reptil.

DISGUSTING DRAWING!

Abomination is one revolting villain, but don't tell him that! The big-headed bully believes that he's better looking than Thor and brainier than Mr Fantastic. Draw your own portrait of Abomination in here.

Don't forget to include the rogue's slimy scales and nasty nails! When you've finished, colour him in.

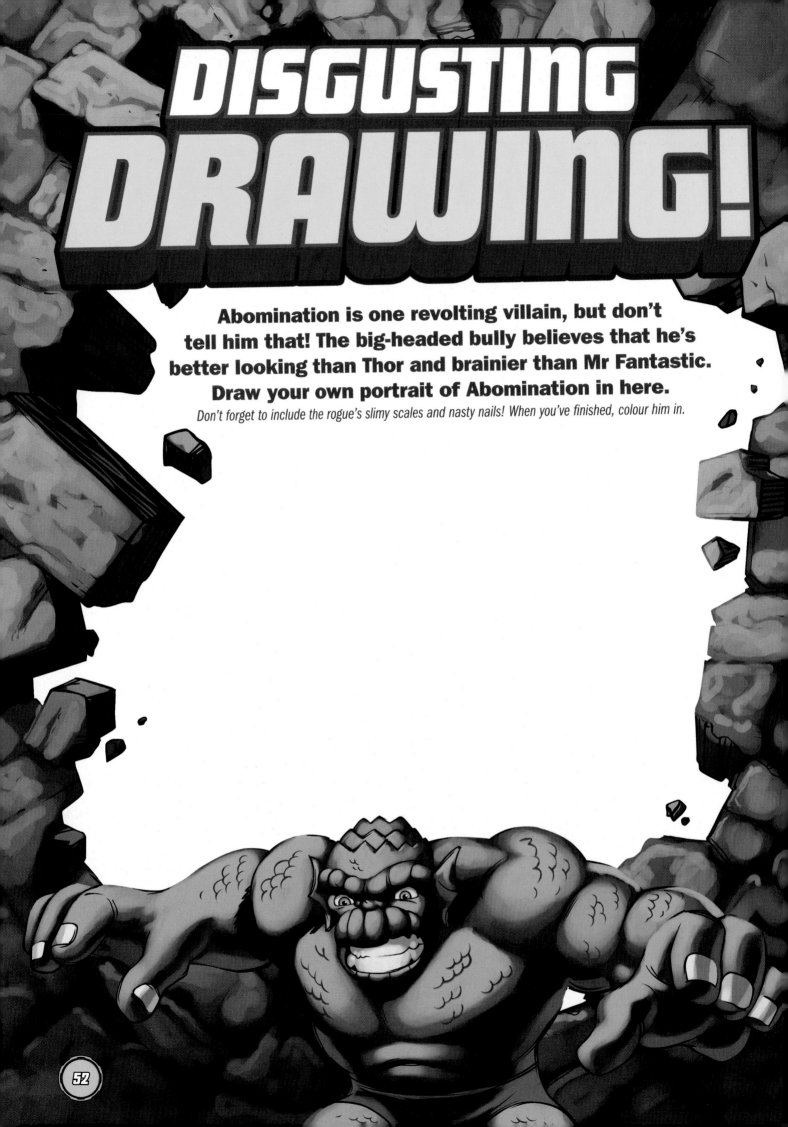

SEARCH THE SENTINELS

The streets are over-run with Sentinels! Doom has dispatched his automated army to create mayhem in the city. Luckily the Super Hero Squad has sent its own man out to stop them. Can you locate him and write down his name?

THE SUPER HERO IS: ....

HOW MANY SENTINELS ARE RAMPAGING THROUGH SUPER HERO CITY? COUNT THEM UP THEN ADD THE TOTAL TO THIS BOX.

CYCLOPS CHASE GAME

1 START

2

3

4. Colossus comes to lend a hand, move forward 3 spaces.

5

11

12

13. Cyclops shows you a shortcut to the villain's hideout. Move forward to 20.

14

15

21

22

23

Trace the Super Hero counters onto a sheet of white card. Colour each disk in, then ask a grown-up to cut them out.

29

30

31

HOW TO PLAY

Four people can join Cyclops' chase game. Choose a counter each and then line them up at the first square. The person who throws the highest number gets to start. Take turns throwing the dice and working your way along the board. The winner will get to the fractal first!

35

36

37. The Silver Surfer points the way to the fractal. Take another go.

Doom and his crew have found one of the Infinity Sword's precious fractals! The Squad is going to have to work together to round up the villains and get the shard back into safe hands.

When it comes to team-work, no one does it better than Cyclops. Grab some friends, choose a Squaddie each, and then report in for duty! This chase game will have you on the edge of your seats as you race to save the day.

6

7. Loki hides the fractal in his throne room. Only move forward when you throw a 6.

8

9. Stop to break up a fight between Thing and Abomination. Miss a turn.

10

16

17

18. Dr Doom summons more reinforcements. Move back 3 spaces.

19

20

24. Hulk adds some extra fighting power. Take another go.

25

26

27. Magneto tries to suck the Helicarrier into his grasp. Miss a go so you can defend it.

28

32

33. The Sentinel army is sent to defeat you. Go back to the start.

34

38

39

40 FINISH

YOU DID IT!

SUPER HERO SQUAD COLOURING POSTER!

The Super Hero Squad is ready for action! Colour in this cool colouring poster using all your most awesome shades. Don't forget to bring to life Hulk's gamma green skin and Wolverine's shiny blue gauntlets.

57

HERO HEAD TO HEAD

TIME TO HERO UP!

ACROSS

1. Expert marksman.
2. Can summon any dinosaur ability.
3. Ultra-flexible science whiz..

DOWN

1. Wields a mighty war hammer.
2. Attacks with optic energy beams.
3. Flies with a hard light harness.

There's a massive rumble going down in Super Hero City! General Ross' toughest Heroes are pitting their wits against Doom's evil henchmen. Who will win the showdown?

Find a friend who's feeling villainous, then grab a pencil each. Ask your pal to look at Doom's crossword panel, while you read General Ross' clues. Set a stopwatch to zero and then see who can complete their crossword the quickest! Every answer sends an extra hero or villain flying into the fray. Will good triumph over evil? The outcome is up to you...

PREPARE TO BE DEFEATED!

ACROSS

1. Shifts her shape to impersonate enemies.

2. Green-gilled monster.

3. Asgard's official troublemaker.

DOWN

1. Eight-limbed menace.

2. Doom's second-in-command.

3. Automated robot army.

FALCON'S QUICK QUIZ

Falcon soars through the sky at unbelievable speed – blink and the birdman is out of sight! How rapid are your reactions? Give the Super Hero's quick quiz a try. If you can answer all ten teasers in less than five minutes, you've got the lightning touch too!

1. Who is the Squad's resident Philosopher?

a. Mr Fantastic
b. Silver Surfer
c. Hulk

2. What is the name of Falcon's pet bird?

a. Redfeather
b. Goldwing
c. Redwing

3. Which friend of the Squaddies works at the Daily Bugle?

a. Spider-Man
b. Nick Fury
c. General Ross

4. Who can turn their body into organic steel?

a. Iron Man
b. Silver Surfer
c. Colossus

5. Whose catchphrase is 'Back off, bub'?

a. Wolverine
b. Cyclops
c. Human Torch

6. Which Squaddie is a fearsome a street-fighter?

a. Hulk
b. Iceman
c. Thing

7. Who attacks with a bow and arrow?

a. Cyclops
b. Mr Fantastic
c. Hawkeye

8. Which Hero has a dishonourable half-brother?

a. Thor
b. Wolverine
c. Invisible Woman

9. Who has the ability to see with thermal vision?

a. Human Torch
b. Iceman
c. Cyclops

10. Which gadget-fan is also the boss of Stark Industries?

a. Mr Fantastic
b. Iron Man
c. Reptil

GRIM GAGS!

Things aren't always miserable at Doom Castle – sometimes the villains cackle the night away, making jokes at each other's expense! Here are some of the sneaky team's most withering wisecracks.

WHAT IS BIG, UGLY AND BOUNCES UP AND DOWN?
ABOMINATION ON A POGO STICK

WHAT VEHICLE DOES DOC OCK DRIVE?
AN ARMOURED CAR

WHAT HAPPENS WHEN VILLAINS HOLD BEAUTY CONTESTS?
NOBODY WINS

WHAT'S SUPER SKRULL'S FAVOURITE PART OF THE JOKE?
THE PUNCH LINE

WHAT KIND OF HORSE DOES LOKI RIDE?
A NIGHT-MARE

HOW MANY BADDIES DOES IT TAKE TO CHANGE A LIGHTBULB?
NONE. THEY LIKE THE DARK

WHAT IS THE BEST THING TO DO IF A SENTINEL BREAKS DOWN YOUR FRONT DOOR?
RUN OUT OF THE BACK DOOR

WHAT'S BLUE, DANGEROUS AND HAS EIGHT WHEELS?
MYSTIQUE ON ROLLER-SKATES

PHOTO

Wanna have your picture taken with the Super Hero Squad? This cool make-it will put you in the frame right next to your Heroes! All you need are some old plastic CD cases and a few art supplies.

To make each frame, you will need:

Empty CD box made of clear plastic
Crayons or felt-tipped pens • Scissors • Pencil
Tracing paper • Thin white card • Sticky tape

What to do

1 Take a CD box and open it up. Take out any paper inserts then stand the box up with the hinge at the top.

2 Find a photo of yourself or draw a self-portrait using crayons or felt-tips. Now ask a grown-up to help you cut the picture out so that it is just a touch smaller than the square of the CD box.

3 Put your photo to one side, then choose one of the Super Hero frames from the opposite page. Trace the frame onto a sheet of thin card. This will sit in the CD box front of your drawing or photo.

4 Colour the Squad frame in, flicking through the pages of this annual to find the right shades for each section.

5 Now fit the frame into the case so that it is facing out of the back of the box, with the hinge still at the top.

6 When the frame is in place, put your photo or picture in behind it. Slide the edges of the picture behind the plastic mounts at the top and bottom of the CD case.

7 You can change your photo as often as you like, but to make sure that it stays put use some short pieces of sticky tape at the back of the frame.

8 Now your super-cool frame is ready to prop up on the mantelpiece or next to your bed!

FANTASTIC

MARVEL® SUPER HERO SQUAD

STAY SCISSOR SAFE!

ALL SUPER HEROES KNOW THAT SCISSORS ARE SHARP. ALWAYS ASK AN ADULT TO HELP YOU WITH CUTTING OUT.

FALCON FIGHTS BACK!

PART ONE

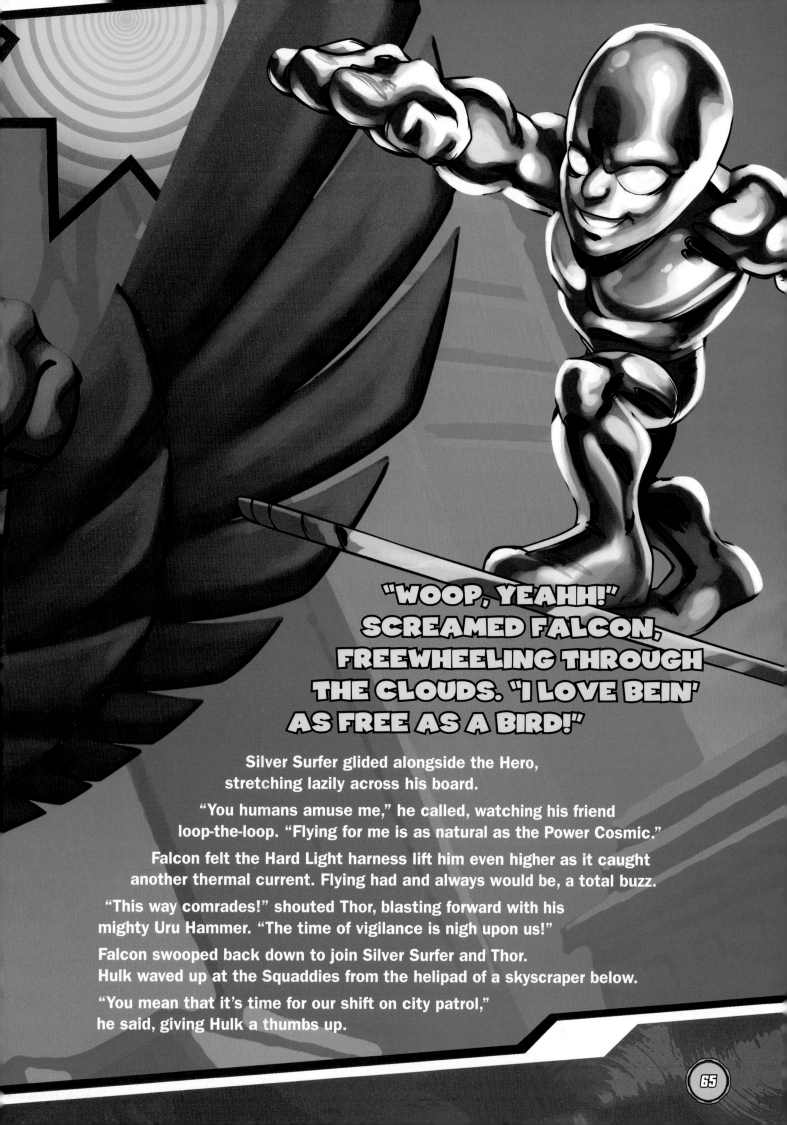

"WOOP, YEAHH!" SCREAMED FALCON, FREEWHEELING THROUGH THE CLOUDS. "I LOVE BEIN' AS FREE AS A BIRD!"

Silver Surfer glided alongside the Hero, stretching lazily across his board.

"You humans amuse me," he called, watching his friend loop-the-loop. "Flying for me is as natural as the Power Cosmic."

Falcon felt the Hard Light harness lift him even higher as it caught another thermal current. Flying had and always would be, a total buzz.

"This way comrades!" shouted Thor, blasting forward with his mighty Uru Hammer. "The time of vigilance is nigh upon us!"

Falcon swooped back down to join Silver Surfer and Thor. Hulk waved up at the Squaddies from the helipad of a skyscraper below.

"You mean that it's time for our shift on city patrol," he said, giving Hulk a thumbs up.

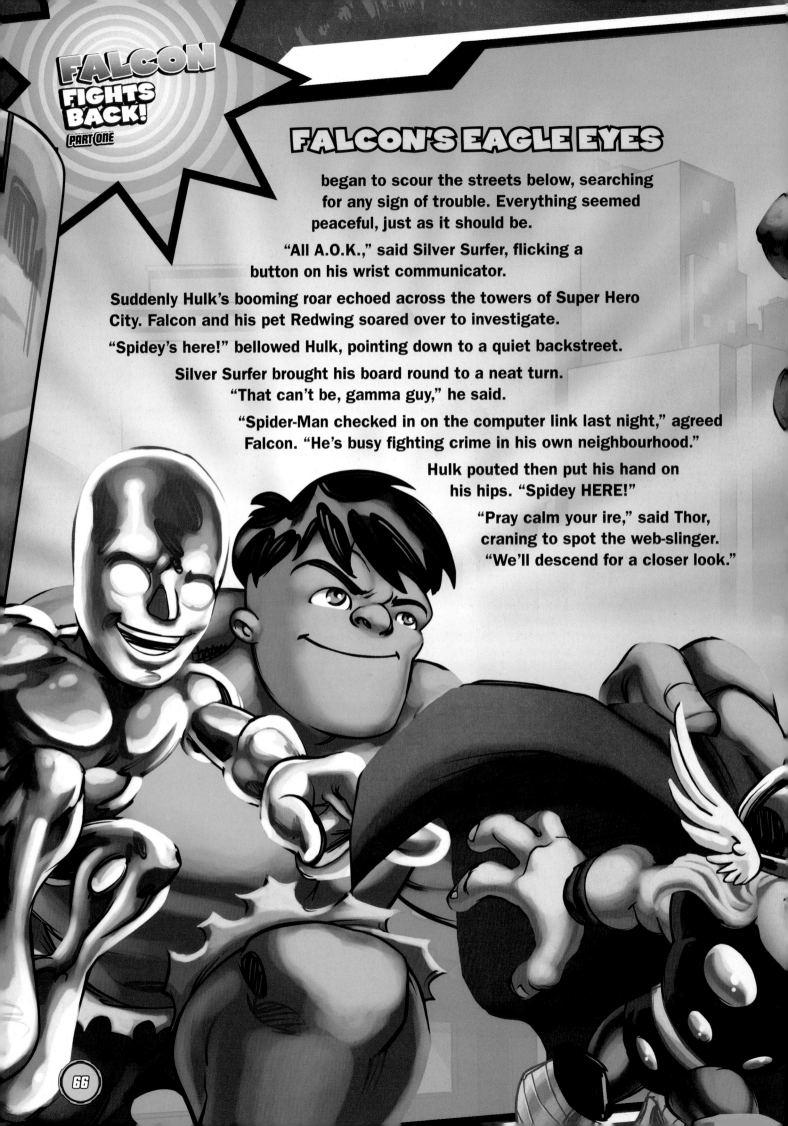

FALCON FIGHTS BACK!
PART ONE

FALCON'S EAGLE EYES

began to scour the streets below, searching for any sign of trouble. Everything seemed peaceful, just as it should be.

"All A.O.K.," said Silver Surfer, flicking a button on his wrist communicator.

Suddenly Hulk's booming roar echoed across the towers of Super Hero City. Falcon and his pet Redwing soared over to investigate.

"Spidey's here!" bellowed Hulk, pointing down to a quiet backstreet.

Silver Surfer brought his board round to a neat turn. "That can't be, gamma guy," he said.

"Spider-Man checked in on the computer link last night," agreed Falcon. "He's busy fighting crime in his own neighbourhood."

Hulk pouted then put his hand on his hips. "Spidey HERE!"

"Pray calm your ire," said Thor, craning to spot the web-slinger. "We'll descend for a closer look."

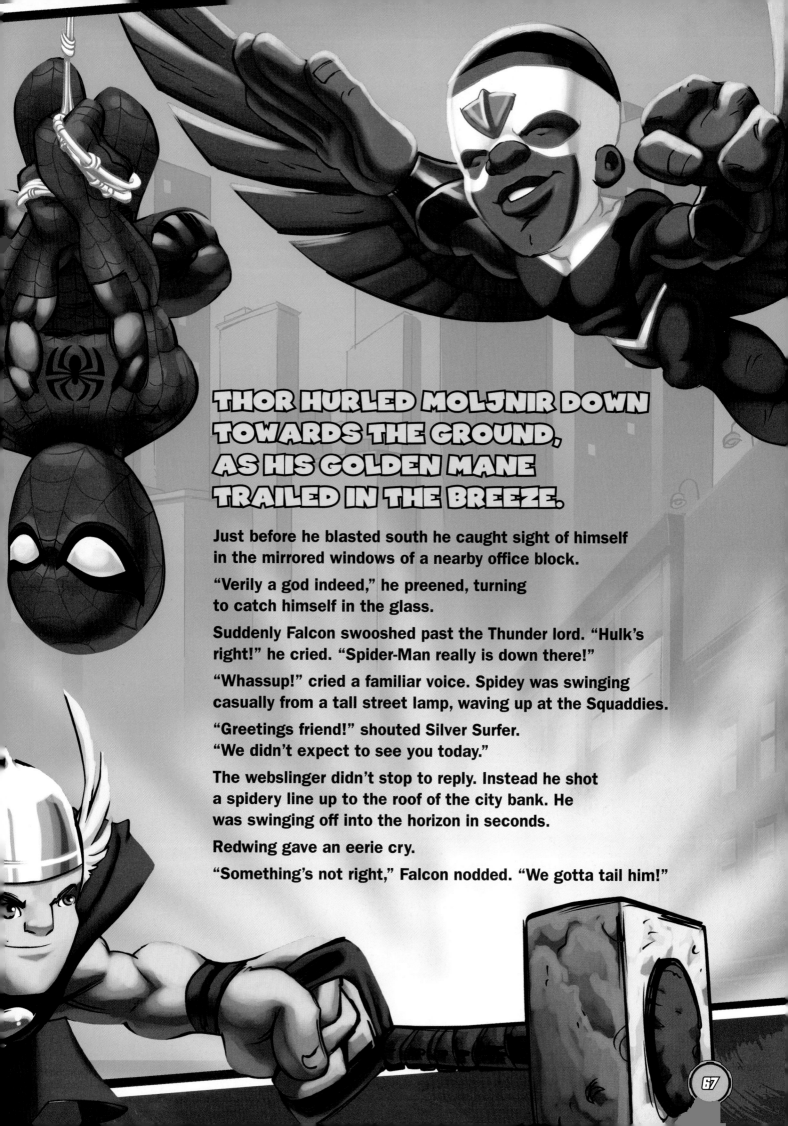

THOR HURLED MOLJNIR DOWN TOWARDS THE GROUND, AS HIS GOLDEN MANE TRAILED IN THE BREEZE.

Just before he blasted south he caught sight of himself in the mirrored windows of a nearby office block.

"Verily a god indeed," he preened, turning to catch himself in the glass.

Suddenly Falcon swooshed past the Thunder lord. "Hulk's right!" he cried. "Spider-Man really is down there!"

"Whassup!" cried a familiar voice. Spidey was swinging casually from a tall street lamp, waving up at the Squaddies.

"Greetings friend!" shouted Silver Surfer. "We didn't expect to see you today."

The webslinger didn't stop to reply. Instead he shot a spidery line up to the roof of the city bank. He was swinging off into the horizon in seconds.

Redwing gave an eerie cry.

"Something's not right," Falcon nodded. "We gotta tail him!"

FALCON FIGHTS BACK!
PART ONE

"PRAY HALT!" BOOMED THOR, CRASHING LEFT AND RIGHT.

The Squaddies were using all their powers to keep up with Spider-Man, but he was as quick as lightning. Every time the crew got closer, the web crawler would dart up the side of a building and disappear from view.

Hulk bounded through the streets below the Heroes, beating his chest with frustration.

"Why won't he stop?" asked Falcon. "Spidey's meant to be one of us!"

Within minutes, the Squaddies had hurtled right across the city.

"Let's touch base with Iron Man," suggested Silver Surfer, watching their pal zig zag out towards the industrial area.

"We've had no contact from Spider-Man here," confirmed their leader from the Helicarrier. "But he is a trusted comrade. He must have a good reason for this behaviour."

REDWING SUDDENLY DROPPED OUT OF THE SKIES, SPIRALLING DOWN TOWARDS THE CITY'S NUCLEAR PLANT.

"Right behind ya, buddy!" cried Falcon, spotting a blur of red and blue flit below them.

The Squaddies touched down in front of the plant entrance, just as Hulk smashed round the corner.

"I'm not feeling positive energy," frowned Silver Surfer. "What's Spidey doing here?"

"Hey guys!" echoed Spider-Man's familiar voice. "This way!"

Falcon led the pursuit. "If Iron Man says we gotta trust him, we gotta trust him."

The Squad followed the direction of Spider-Man's calls, clambering through doorways then sprinting down long, grey corridors Within moments, the crew were standing inside a dark chamber.

"Hulk wanna go home!" bawled the mutant, searching for the door.

BAAANNNGGG!

The cast iron door slammed with a thump!

"Some traitor has locked us in!" cried Thor.
"Spider-Man is not to be surveyed!"

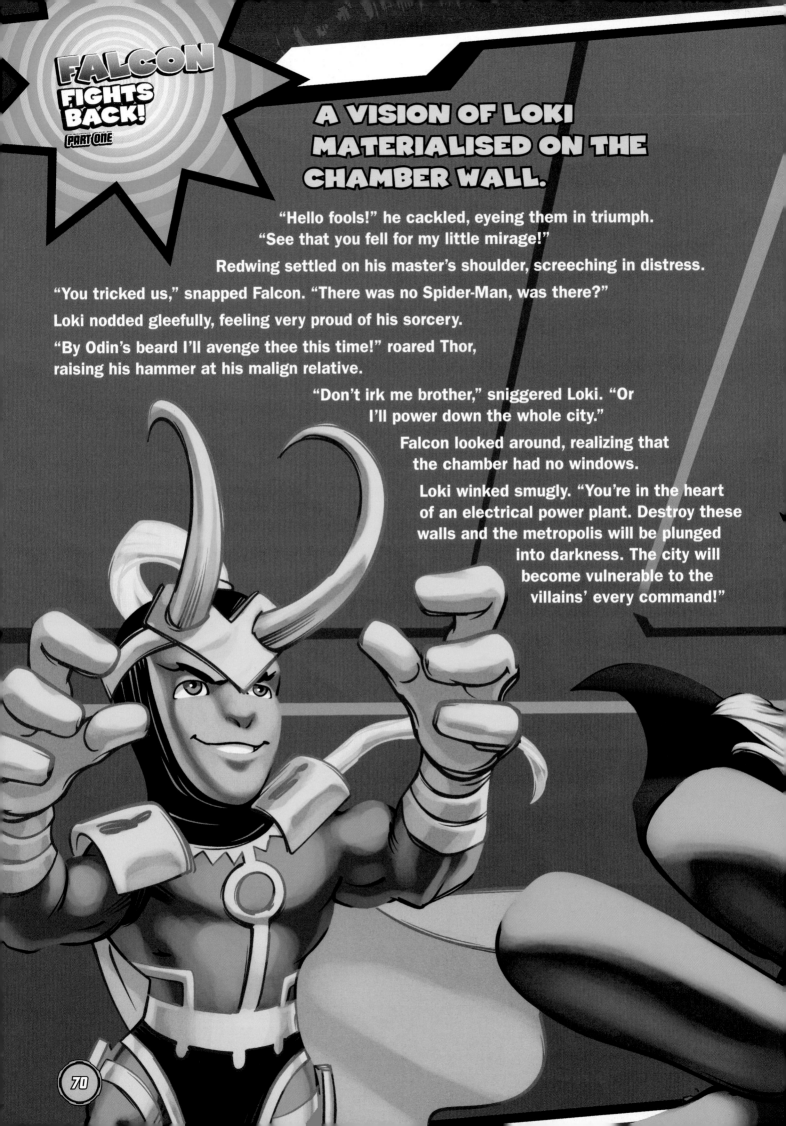

FALCON FIGHTS BACK!
PART ONE

A VISION OF LOKI MATERIALISED ON THE CHAMBER WALL.

"Hello fools!" he cackled, eyeing them in triumph. "See that you fell for my little mirage!"

Redwing settled on his master's shoulder, screeching in distress.

"You tricked us," snapped Falcon. "There was no Spider-Man, was there?"

Loki nodded gleefully, feeling very proud of his sorcery.

"By Odin's beard I'll avenge thee this time!" roared Thor, raising his hammer at his malign relative.

"Don't irk me brother," sniggered Loki. "Or I'll power down the whole city."

Falcon looked around, realizing that the chamber had no windows.

Loki winked smugly. "You're in the heart of an electrical power plant. Destroy these walls and the metropolis will be plunged into darkness. The city will become vulnerable to the villains' every command!"

SILVER SURFER BLINKED INTO HIS WRIST COMMUNICATOR.

The monitor was completely dead.

"No reception?" asked Loki in mock sympathy. "This chamber is encased by three metres of solid steel. Maybe that isn't helping."

"Me get YOU!" thundered Hulk, beating at his chest.

The Squaddies leapt to restrain the mighty mutant's arms and feet.

"We've got to stay calm," urged Falcon. "Our very strength could threaten Super Hero City's power supply."

Loki nodded, then burst into joyful giggles. "While you figure this one out, we villains are off to have some fun!"

Thor trembled with rage as the picture began to disappear.

"Magneto's locked down the exits," added Loki. "So don't try anything silly."

**TO BE CONTINUED...
TURN TO PAGE 90**

PUZZLE PATROL

A witness has reported a shady figure lurking round the city pier, so the Super Hero Squad have come out in force! Hulk has powered up the turbo hovercraft and Spider-Man has switched on the jet guns. Watch out villains – the Squad are on your tail!

There are **six** differences between these pictures. Study them both carefully, and then circle each of the differences with a coloured Biro or felt-tipped pen.

NICK'S NOTES

Looks like Nick Fury's in some serious kinda trouble! He's scribbled a note to the Super Hero Squad, but parts of the message have been blotted out. Use the picture clues to help you write in the missing words and get the Squad on the case!

I need your help! A devious plot by _____ and

_____ has lured me away from Super Hero

_____ . Now I'm trapped in the dungeons

 of _____ !  _____ is guarding

the cell door while the rest of the

_____ are out causing trouble.

Tell _____ to raise the alarm in the

_____ . He's got to send in _____ and the

rest of the  _____ right away!

Over and out, Nick Fury

WATCH WOLVIE GO!

Wolverine is patrolling the City in his Fastball Special – a turbo motorbike with awesome engine power! The super-scrapper has been so busy fighting crime tonight that he's managed to cruise several blocks away from the rest of the Squad.

Help Wolvie get back to his buddies by tracing a route through this grid. Put your finger on the start then follow the words that best describe the Super Hero Squad all the way to the end.

START

GOOD	FEARLESS	SPITEFUL	DESPICABLE	SCARY	TREACHEROUS	BOSSY	BITTER
WEEDY	STRONG	EVIL	SHIFTY	ROTTEN	VAIN	UNPLEASANT	FOUL
MEAN	NOBLE	VALIANT	DARING	HORRID	BULLYING	LOATHSOME	WRONG
COWARDLY	DEVIOUS	MONSTROUS	COURAGEOUS	LOYAL	DECENT	HONEST	TYRANNICAL
WEAK	SLY	ANGRY	FIENDISH	CREEPY	FALSE	TOUGH	DEMANDING
NASTY	GREEDY	SHAMELESS	DISHONEST	SELFISH	BAD	BOLD	GALLANT
CRUEL	SNEAKY	ARROGANT	UNDERHAND	VILE	MERCIFUL	BIG HEADED	BRAVE
SCHEMING	CRIMINAL	UNKIND	CALLOUS	WICKED	DECEITFUL	VILLAINOUS	HEROIC

FINISH

DON'T FORGET!

**Stick with the heroic words.
Villainous talk only spells trouble!**

SILVER SURFER'S SCRAPBOOK

Silver Surfer's had an awesome year hanging out with his super-human friends! When he's not been mellowing out back at base, the Sentinel of the Spaceways has been throwing sky-high tricks on his mirror board. Take a sneak peek into his scrapbook and then draw in your memories of the year.

Patrolling the streets of Super Hero City. I love this town!

A different type of surfin' – watching Wolvie, Human Torch and Spider-Man snowboarding was sooo much fun!

This pic of me was taken just after we'd defeated another of Doom's crackpot plots. Just a regular week in Super Hero City...

This snap of Magneto always makes me chuckle! The dude wouldn't stop boasting about his powers of magnetism... until half the hardware in the area got attracted to his head!

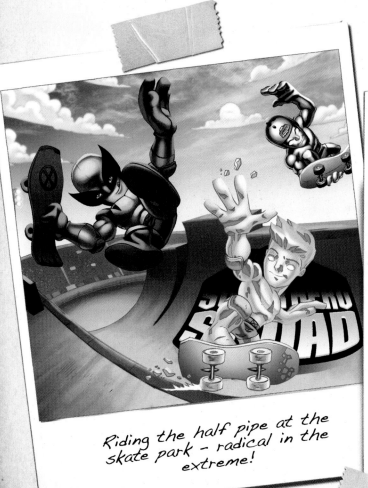

Riding the half pipe at the skate park - radical in the extreme!

Draw your favourite memory in here.
Don't forget to add a caption too!

WHO'S WHO CLUES

How well do you know your Heroes and Villains? Study the picture and word clues that run down each ID chain and then write the correct names in the panels at the bottom.

1

PART-TIME MEMBER OF THE SUPER HERO SQUAD

SCALES UP VERTICAL WALLS WITH GREAT EASE

MOST LIKELY TO SAY: 'JUST THOUGHT I'D SWING BY'

THE HERO IS..

2

MAD SCIENTIST IN DARK GLASSES

CAN EXTEND ROBOTIC ARMS TO GREAT LENGTHS

MOST LIKELY TO SAY: 'I'M FULLY ARMED!'

THE VILLAIN IS..

3

SHAPE SHIFTER WITH YELLOW EYES

CAN IMPERSONATE ANYONE SHE CHOOSES

MOST LIKELY TO SAY: 'RESIST ME AT YOUR PERIL!'

THE VILLAIN IS..

4

YOUNG MUTANT WHO LOVES PLAYING PRANKS

HALTS EVIL WITH BLASTS OF ARCTIC COLD ICE

MOST LIKELY TO SAY: 'THIS IS GETTING WAY TOO HOT FOR ME!'

HERO IS..

STORMING IN TO SAVE THE DAY

What a terrific trio! The combined force of Thor, Hawkeye and Hulk will blast through any opposition. Villains watch out, these heavyweights mean business.

Turn this colour-by-numbers activity into an eye-catching Super Hero picture! Use the key below to help you choose the right colours to bring the team to life.

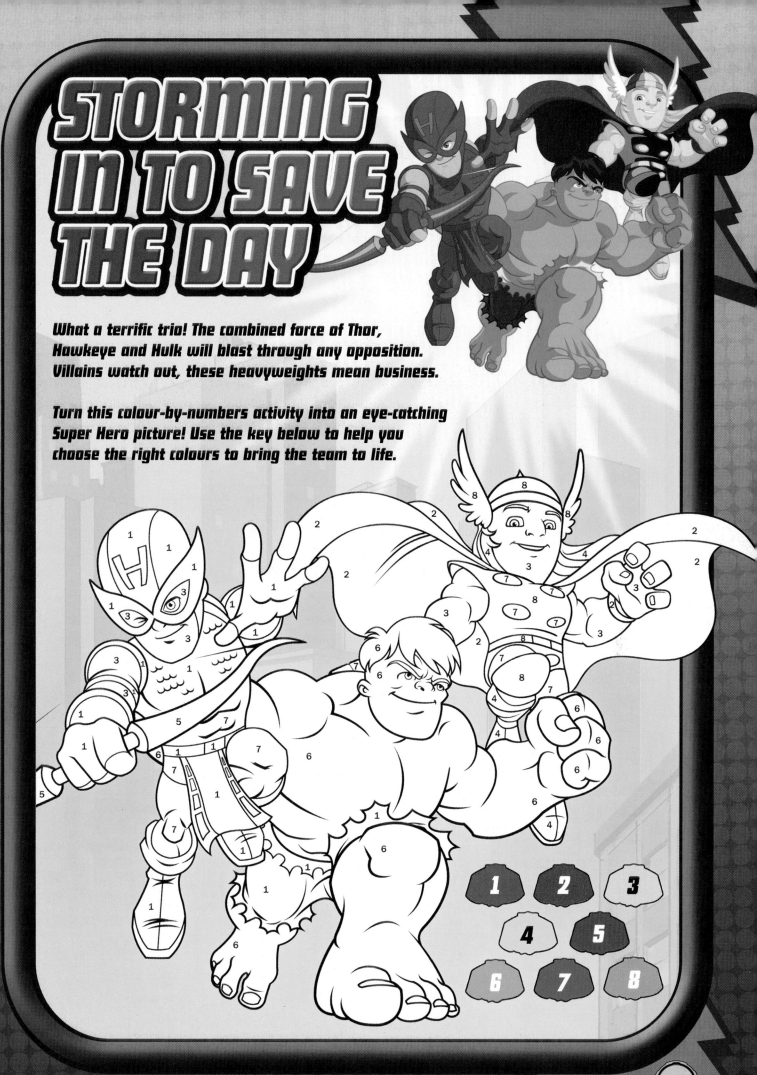

THE SUPER HERO NEEDS YOU!

Nick Fury's got a vacancy for one more Hero – could you be the person to fill the job? Think about the qualities you could bring to the world's most respected crime-fighting force, then start designing your own superhuman alter-ego today!

Awesome Abilities

Every Super Hero worth their salt has got a unique ability that sets them a cut above the regular tough guys. Tick the qualities that you'd like your Super Hero to possess. You can choose from the list below or think up something totally new!

- X-ray vision
- Unrivalled strength
- Ultra-flexibility
- Poison fingers
- Wall-shattering screams
- Supersonic flight
- Control of the weather
- Temperature resistance
- Wall-crawling
- Turbo swimming
- Genius intelligence
- Explosive attacks
- Radiation

My Super Hero powers would be

....

Name Game

The greatest Super Heroes all have names that sum up their skills – you need to sound like a powerhouse who crooks won't forget in a hurry. Who would cross Iron Man, Wolverine or Human Torch?

My Super Hero name would be

....

SQUAD

It's **costume time!**

What would your alter ego look like? Draw a punchy portrait in here.

MARVEL
SUPER HERO
SQUAD

ODD SQUAD OUT

You'll need the accuracy of Hawkeye and the brains of Mr Fantastic to crack this puzzle! The Super Hero Squad is on the attack, but only one of the pictures on this page is the real deal. Study all five then circle the one that is an exact match to the shot at the top.

HERO AT HOME

You don't have to be superhuman to enjoy breathtaking Hero action! Iron Man wants to share his top five tips for having fun with your friends at home. Whether it's after school or on the weekend, he'll prove that anyone can Hero Up in their own bedroom, park or back garden...

1 Raid the dressing up box then put together your own super-cool costume. Heroes love capes, helmets and awesome utility belts. Use fabric paints to customise plain T-shirts or make masks out of cardboard.

2 Get gadget-tastic! Gear yourself up with all the latest technology. Transform toy walkie-talkies, old mobile phones or broken personal stereos into communication devices for radioing your Hero pals.

3 Think up a memorable catchphrase! When Thing shouts 'it's clobberin' time!' every one knows to get out of the way fast! What will you shout when you rush into danger?

4 Make yourself a secret base. When you're under attack from a merciless enemy, you need somewhere to rest and regroup. Make a camp at the bottom of the garden or transform your bedroom into Hero HQ.

5 Devise a secret code for communication with your fellow Squaddies. Work out a series of signs so that you know when it's time to attack, or agree some code words that will outsmart any villains within earshot.

DARING DOZEN WORDSEARCH

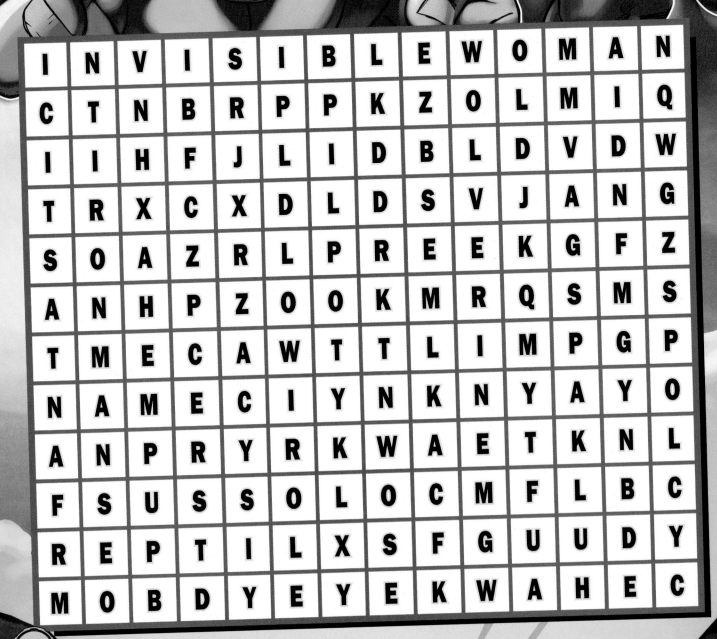

I	N	V	I	S	I	B	L	E	W	O	M	A	N
C	T	N	B	R	P	P	K	Z	O	L	M	I	Q
I	I	H	F	J	L	I	D	B	L	D	V	D	W
T	R	X	C	X	D	L	D	S	V	J	A	N	G
S	O	A	Z	R	L	P	R	E	E	K	G	F	Z
A	N	H	P	Z	O	O	K	M	R	Q	S	M	S
T	M	E	C	A	W	T	T	L	I	M	P	G	P
N	A	M	E	C	I	Y	N	K	N	Y	A	Y	O
A	N	P	R	Y	R	K	W	A	E	T	K	N	L
F	S	U	S	S	O	L	O	C	M	F	L	B	C
R	E	P	T	I	L	X	S	F	G	U	U	D	Y
M	O	B	D	Y	E	Y	E	K	W	A	H	E	C

This wordsearch grid is packed with Super Heroes! Use the picture clues to help you write in 12 Squaddies and then highlight their names on the letter grid. You'll need to be sharp-eyed – the names could be printed in any direction. Watch out for letters running in reverse and tricky diagonals!

BAD ANAGRAMS

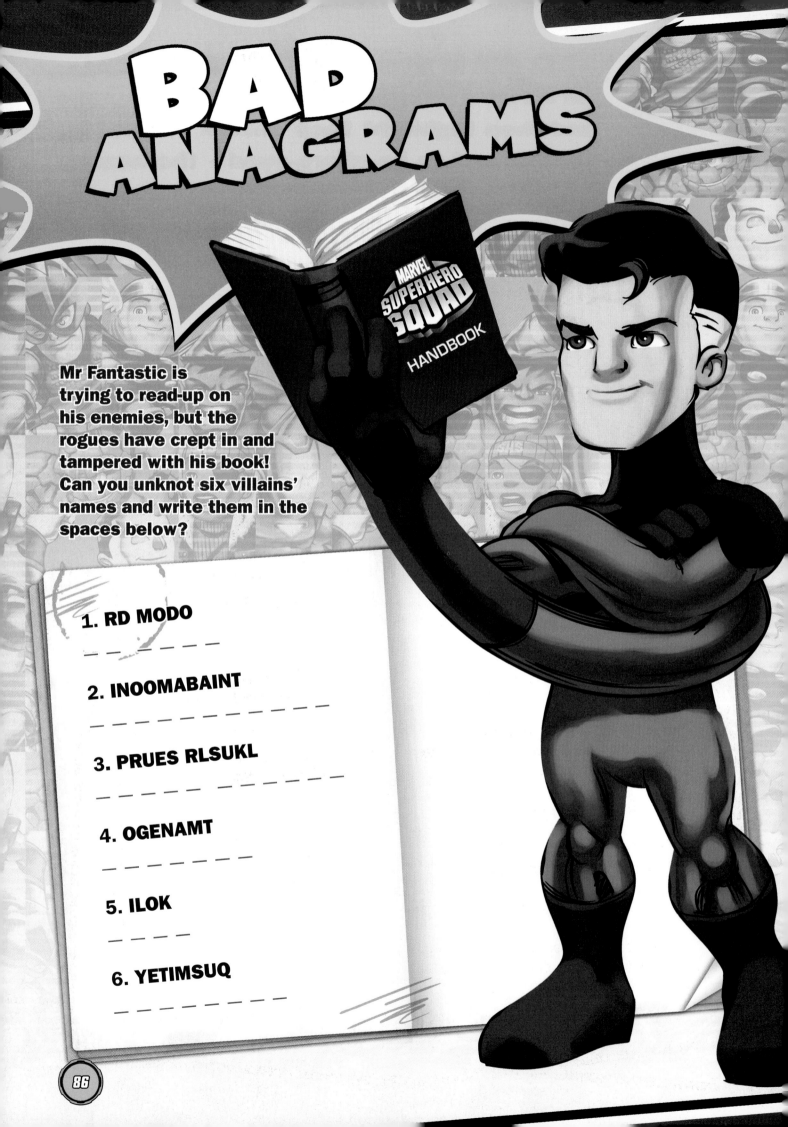

Mr Fantastic is trying to read-up on his enemies, but the rogues have crept in and tampered with his book! Can you unknot six villains' names and write them in the spaces below?

1. RD MODO

_ _ _ _ _ _

2. INOOMABAINT

_ _ _ _ _ _ _ _ _ _ _

3. PRUES RLSUKL

_ _ _ _ _ _ _ _ _ _

4. OGENAMT

_ _ _ _ _ _ _

5. ILOK

_ _ _ _

6. YETIMSUQ

_ _ _ _ _ _ _ _

SPIDEY'S SECRETS

HE'S THE ULTIMATE
CRIME-FIGHTER –
A LIVING LEGEND
WHOSE REPUTATION
ALONE GETS
VILLAINS QUAKING
IN THEIR BOOTS!
SPIDER-MAN HAS GOT
THE BRAINS, THE MUSCLE
AND THE MOVES! TEST YOUR KNOWLEDGE
OF THE HERO BY TAKING ON THIS TRUE OR
FALSE CHALLENGE. THE ANSWERS ARE
WAITING FOR YOU AT THE BACK OF THE BOOK

1. His webs are stronger than
   any man-made rope.
   True ☐   False ☐

2. He can fly.
   True ☐   False ☐

3. He has a sixth spider sense
   that allows him to detect danger.
   True ☐   False ☐

4. He has super-fast reflexes.
   True ☐   False ☐

5. He feeds on bugs and
   small insects.
   True ☐   False ☐

6. He was transformed after being
   bitten by a radioactive spider.
   True ☐   False ☐

7. He only joins the Squad's
   night missions.
   True ☐   False ☐

8. His supreme balance allows him
   to scale sheer walls with ease.
   True ☐   False ☐

9. He's a part-time member of
   the Super Hero Squad.
   True ☐   False ☐

10. His spidey eyes can blind those
    that stare straight at them.
    True ☐   False ☐

HOW MANY DID YOU GET
RIGHT? SCORE OVER
SEVEN AND YOU'RE A
TOP-NOTCH SPIDEY FAN!

AMAZING TRANSFORMATIONS

Reptil is unstoppable when he uses his prehistoric sunstone to morph into dinosaur form! The mighty mutant can suddenly gain the brawn of a Brontosaurus or the tearing teeth of a Tyrannosaurus Rex.

Now you've got the chance to bring Reptil's transformation to life by making this knockout moving poster! Just slide the poster backwards and forwards to show the Squaddie leaping into action. Your friends will be amazed at Reptil's superhuman speed!

YOU WILL NEED
A3 sheet of thin black card - Ruler - Pencil
Scissors - A3 sheet of thick white card
Paper glue - A3 white paper - Felt-tips or crayons

1 Lay the A3 black card on the table and then mark out a 4cm border at the top and bottom with a ruler.

2 Turn the ruler vertically and then use it to mark out regular ruler-length strips all along the middle section of the black card. Cut off any uneven length left at the end with paper scissors.

3 Very carefully cut out every other vertical strip on the card, making sure you don't snip over the edges. When you have finished the card should look like the black bars of a prison cell window (right).

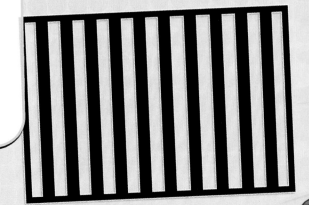

4

Take the sheet of thick white card and then dot it with glue all along the top and bottom edges. Gently lay the black bars over the top of the card, sticking them in place.

5

Now take a piece of A3 paper and slide it very slowly in between the black bars and the white base card (below).

6

Use a pencil to draw in a picture of Reptil in his human form onto the white paper that's visible in between the bars. Use the images on this page to give you inspiration, then colour your artwork in.

7

Slowly move the picture of Reptil to the right so that it is hidden by the bars. On this new clean space draw in a picture of the Hero in dino-form, then colour that in too.

8

When you've finished, move the sheet backwards and forwards as quickly as you can. Reptil will make a dino-mite transformation right before your eyes!

Even Super Heroes need to be safe with scissors! If Wolverine's not around, get a grown-up to help you with any cutting.

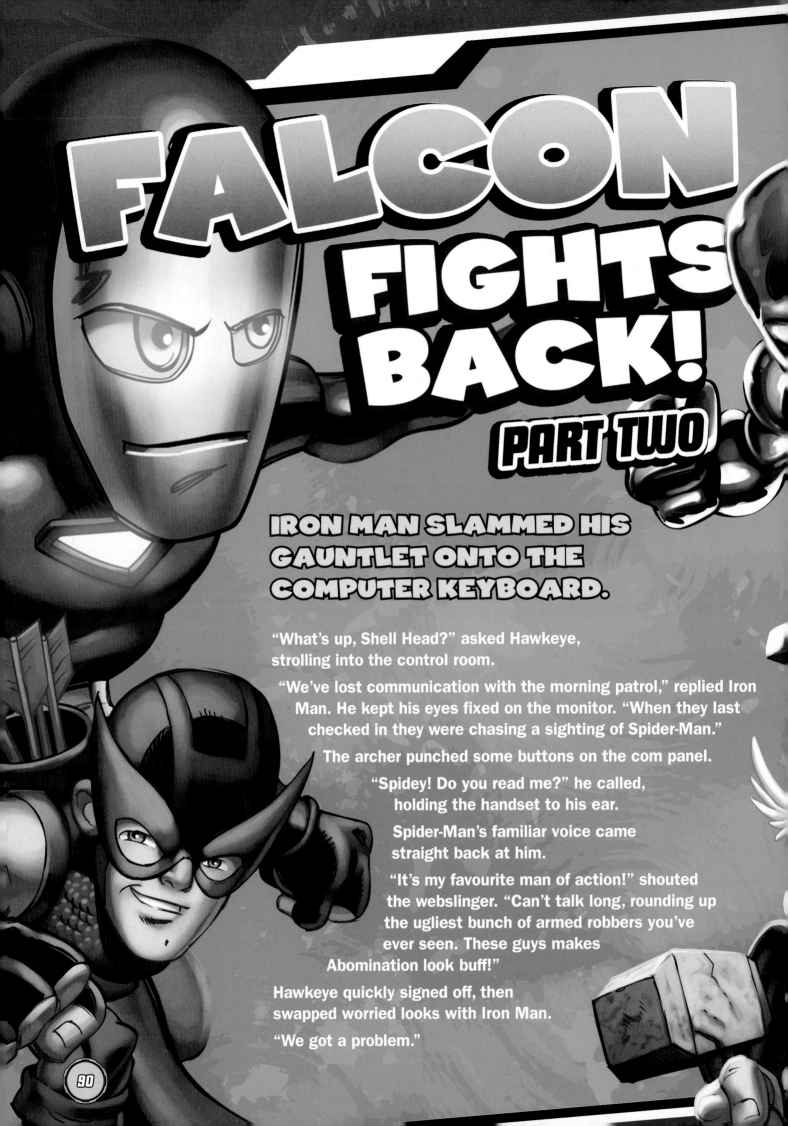

FALCON FIGHTS BACK!

PART TWO

IRON MAN SLAMMED HIS GAUNTLET ONTO THE COMPUTER KEYBOARD.

"What's up, Shell Head?" asked Hawkeye, strolling into the control room.

"We've lost communication with the morning patrol," replied Iron Man. He kept his eyes fixed on the monitor. "When they last checked in they were chasing a sighting of Spider-Man."

The archer punched some buttons on the com panel.

"Spidey! Do you read me?" he called, holding the handset to his ear.

Spider-Man's familiar voice came straight back at him.

"It's my favourite man of action!" shouted the webslinger. "Can't talk long, rounding up the ugliest bunch of armed robbers you've ever seen. These guys makes Abomination look buff!"

Hawkeye quickly signed off, then swapped worried looks with Iron Man.

"We got a problem."

THINGS WERE GETTING TENSE INSIDE THE POWER PLANT.

"Come on Silver Surfer, you can do it!" pressed Falcon.

The sky-rider channelled all his cosmic powers at the chamber door. Red energy blasted the metalwork, but nothing seemed to shift it.

Falcon groaned as another of Loki's visions magically appeared on the cell wall. This time Magneto had decided to make an appearance.

"Nice try, board boy!" he mocked. "I've blocked this door with enough metalwork to keep you trapped here forever."

Falcon paced round in circles. "You don't scare us, helmet head!"

"Verily he speaks the truth," added Thor. "Iron Man and the rest of the Squad will be here to release us in the blink of an eye."

FALCON FIGHTS BACK!
PART TWO

MAGNETO FLASHED AN INNOCENT SMILE.

"If the rest of the Squad turn out to rescue you," he asked. "Who will save the good citizens of Super Hero City?"

The vision cut out, then switched to a view of the centre of town. Falcon cringed as Doom and the rest of the villains rampaged through the streets, terrorising innocent passersby.

"What devilry is this?" bellowed Thor. "They've outwitted us fair and square."

Hulk's body began to shake with rage.

"ME GONNA GET OUT!" he roared.

"The rest of the team must go and save the city," announced Falcon. "If we're going to save ourselves, we've got to use our heads."

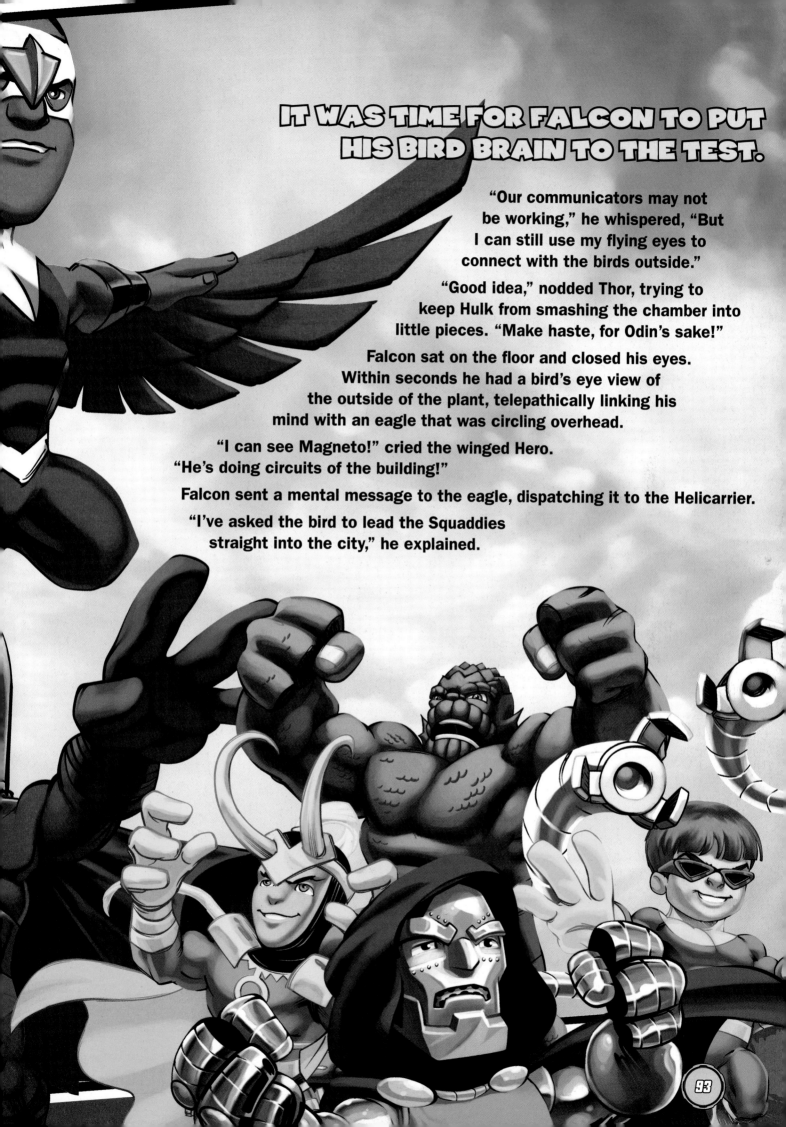

IT WAS TIME FOR FALCON TO PUT HIS BIRD BRAIN TO THE TEST.

"Our communicators may not be working," he whispered, "But I can still use my flying eyes to connect with the birds outside."

"Good idea," nodded Thor, trying to keep Hulk from smashing the chamber into little pieces. "Make haste, for Odin's sake!"

Falcon sat on the floor and closed his eyes. Within seconds he had a bird's eye view of the outside of the plant, telepathically linking his mind with an eagle that was circling overhead.

"I can see Magneto!" cried the winged Hero. "He's doing circuits of the building!"

Falcon sent a mental message to the eagle, dispatching it to the Helicarrier.

"I've asked the bird to lead the Squaddies straight into the city," he explained.

"GUARDING THOSE BUFFOONS IS ALMOST TOO EASY FOR THE MASTER OF MAGNETISM," SNEERED MAGNETO.

Doom's second-in-command sauntered smugly round the perimeter of the power plant, wondering what mayhem his cronies were causing over in the city.

BANG! BANG!

BANG!

The villain could hear a repeated knocking ring out from deep inside the Squaddies' prison chamber.

"Sounds like they're getting uncomfortable in there," Magneto laughed. "How satisfying!"

BANG!

When the banging stopped, the rogue couldn't resist putting his ear to the thick metal door. Right on cue, the Squaddies began taunting him and calling out names.

"How dare they talk about me like that?" he shouted.

Magneto raised a hand up to the metal vault, pulling the barriers apart.

BACK AT THE HELICARRIER, IRON MAN WAS GRAPPLING WITH A DILEMMA.

"We've got to rescue our guys!" pressed Hawkeye, heading for the door.

"The needs of our citizens must come first," Iron Man argued, looking up at the main computer console. The sudden crime wave that had taken over the city was getting out of hand.

Before the Heroes could fight it out, a blip appeared on the radar screen. The blip seemed to be moving closer and closer to the Helicarrier.

"It's a bird!" gasped Iron Man, opening the docking hatch.

The eagle swept straight into the control room, then perch on a glass table. Hawkeye sensed this was something to do with Falcon. He gasped as the bird began to scratch letters on the table with its talons.

IT'S A TRAP! SAVE THE CITY FIRST

"That's the sign we've been waiting for," said Iron Man, "Time to Hero Up!"

95

FALCON FIGHTS BACK!
PART TWO

BACK AT THE POWER PLANT, MAGNETO WAS GETTING MAD.

Who dares to denounce me?" bellowed the arch-villain. The purple crook used all his powers of magnetism to force open the massive door blocking the Squaddies' exit. It was just what Falcon had planned.

Magneto stormed into the chamber. Thor, Silver Surfer and Hulk all stood braced and ready.

"Where's the other one?" sniped the villain, turning his head left and right.

Suddenly Falcon plunged from the ceiling, swooping down onto Magneto's head. Redwing circled beside him, jabbing the baddie with his beak and claws.

"I thought I'd drop in and say hi!" grinned the soldier, motioning for his buddies to run out the door.

"Get off me!" bawled Magneto.

"You're right," winked Falcon. "We're poles apart!"

RIGHT ON CUE, THOR LIFTED OFF HIS HELMET AND PLACED IT NEXT TO MAGNETO'S HEAD.

The villain found himself being dragged out of the door, his helmet stuck fast to the polished metal.

Hulk led the way, trying not to bash the doors off their hinges.

"Well done big guy," grinned Falcon. "We don't want to risk the city's electricity supply now that we're this close to freedom!"

Thor pulled the screaming scoundrel across the industrial plant, finally stopping outside an iron foundry on the edge of town.

"Loki will curse you for this!" warned Magneto.

"Tis that so?" asked Thor. "Have at thee vile dog!"

Silver Surfer and Falcon pried open the doors to the metalworks. With one swing of his hammer the Thunder God had sent Magneto hurtling inside.

"That's the end of him for a while," grinned Falcon. "Now let's help save our city!"

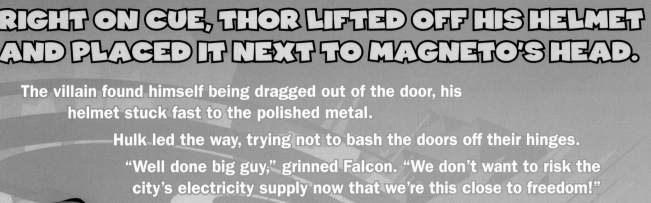

THE END

PRACTICE MAKES PERFECT!

Iron Man works the Squad hard when it's time for a workout! The gang always rehearse their toughest battles moves over and over again so that they're ready to Hero Up the instant that they're needed.

Take a look at the patterns of Heroes below and then draw in the right move at the end of each sequence.

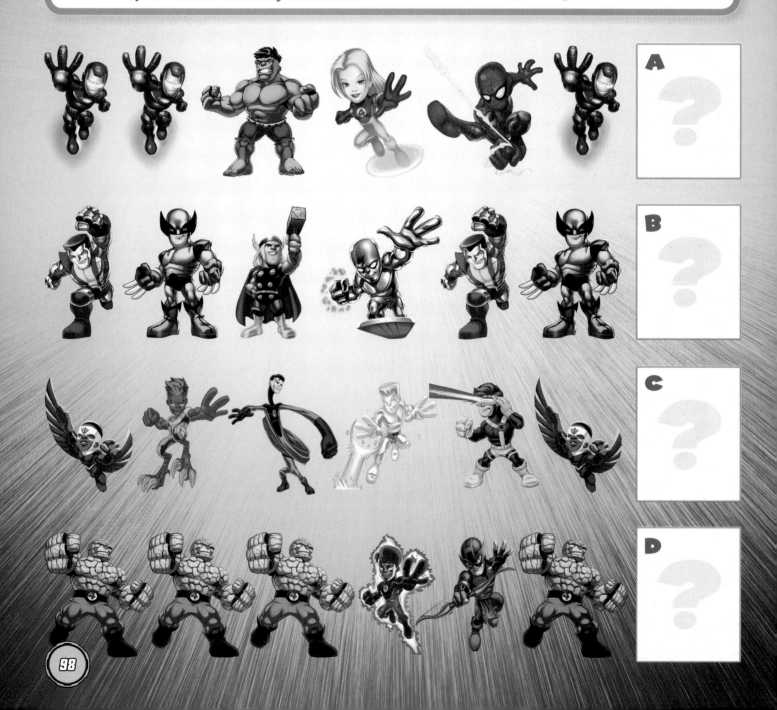

A ?

B ?

C ?

D ?

SECRET SQUAD

The Super Hero Squad have to be alert at all times – you never know when a villain might be snooping nearby! Luckily Mr Fantastic has put his mighty brainpower to use by devising a secret code to stop Dr Doom finding their plans.

When they want to keep things top secret, the Squaddies write using symbols instead of letters. Can you crack their Hero code? All the letters in the alphabet are arranged in the key below.

When Mr Fantastic wants to write a message, he takes away each letter and writes the symbol for it instead. A becomes ↳ right through to Z ⇦... it's as easy as A, B, C!

An urgent memo has only just been released to all Squad members. See if you can work out what it says.

Write your answer in here

_____!

KEY

A = ↳   N = ↰
B = ⇄   O = ↶
C = ↵   P = ↷
D = ↤   Q = ↺
E = ↥   R = ↻
F = ↦   S = ⤬
G = ↧   T = ⌃
H = ↩   U = ⌄
I = ⇉   V = ⌐
J = ⇈   W = ⌐
K = ⇊   X = ⇧
L = ∩   Y = ⇧
M = ∪   Z = ⇦

SENTINEL STORY

Rrrrring! The alarm clock rattled on the table next to

_____'s bunk. 'Just another day in

Super Hero City!' bellowed _____

pulling back the covers. _____ took a

peek out of the window of the Helicarrier. Everything looked calm

and peaceful down on the streets below.

_____ strolled into

the rest area. _____

and _____ were eating

_____ for breakfast, while

_____ was busy working out in the

Squad gym. Suddenly _____ appeared

on the flat screen, shouting 'Calling all Squaddies!'.

_____,

_____ and

_____ all gathered round the

TV. Pictures flashed up showing one of Doom's Sentinels

wreaking havoc in the _____

area of the City. It was time to Hero Up! Before leaving

you grabbed a couple of things you might need to stop the

giant robot – a _____ and a

_____

In seconds you were _____

through the air next to _____

the rest of the Squaddies all following behind you. By

now, the Sentinel was marching down the main street,

blasting _____ and smashing

_____ Terrified citizens hid

behind _____ as the robot

thundered past. The Super Hero Squad soon had the

machine surrounded. _____

pelted its head, while _____ and

_____ both grabbed on to a giant

leg. When the robot kept on marching, you knew it was time to

use your unique _____ super power.

You _____ the Sentinel with your

_____ stopping him in his tracks!

Everybody cheered as you and

_____ worked together to

disable the robot. _____

used their _____ powers

to _____ and disable the

super-droid's power supply. 'Good team work gang!' said

_____

EXAMPLE 1

In seconds you were *flying* through the air next to *Falcon*,

the rest of the Squaddies all following behind you. By now, the

Sentinel was marching down the main street, blasting *cars*

and smashing *shop windows*.

EXAMPLE 2

In seconds you were *gliding* through the air next

to *Silver Surfer*, the rest of the Squaddies

all following behind you. By now, the Sentinel

was marching down the main street, blasting

buildings and smashing *the ground*.

TRANSLATOR GAME

WHEN THOR SPEAKS EVERYBODY LISTENS - BUT NO ONE CAN UNDERSTAND A WORD! THE HAMMER-WIELDING GOLDEN BOY CAN'T HELP USING THE ANCIENT NORDIC SAYINGS FROM HIS HOMETOWN OF ASGARD. THINGS HAVE GOT SO CONFUSING, WOLVERINE HAS DECIDED TO MAKE A MINI DICTIONARY OF HIS PAL'S FAVOURITE PHRASES.

Read Thor's words then draw a line to match them up with Wolvie's Super Hero translations.

1. Have at thee, vile dog!

A. I don't like this situation at all!

2. What devilry is this?

B. Time to strike!

3. By my Nordic nose, your stench is nigh overpowering.

C. What's going on here?

4. Forsooth, Mjolnir's work is done.

D. Take that, rascal!

5. Odin would weep at such a sight!

E. Give back the Fractal, villain!

6. Verily, it's hammer time!

F. The work of evil chokes me up!

7. Methinkith this stinkith.

G. Job done.

8. Thou evil miscreant! Unhand your stole Fractal!

H. You smell terrible!

LOKI'S LAIR

COLOSSUS HAS HAD ENOUGH OF LOKI'S MEDDLING MISCHIEF! THE SNEAKY GREEN SORCERER HAS BEEN CASTING ALL KINDS OF MALICIOUS SPELLS OVER THE GOOD CITIZENS OF SUPER HERO CITY.

Help Colossus storm Loki's hideout, guiding him past dead-ends and blind alleys along the way.

FINISH

MUDDLED MAGNETO!

I AM THE MASTER OF MAGNETISM!

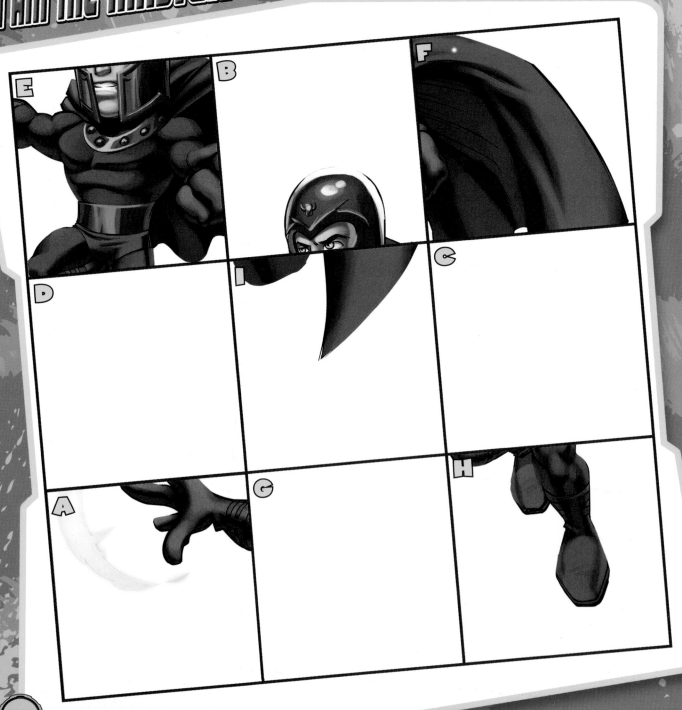

THIS BITTER AND TWISTED VILLAIN'S UNRULY POWERS HAVE MANAGED TO GET HIM IN A SCRAMBLE! USE YOUR SKETCHING SKILLS TO DRAW MAGNETO BACK TOGETHER AGAIN. EACH OF THE SQUARES ON THE GRID IS LABELLED FROM A THROUGH TO I. CAREFULLY COPY THE DETAILS IN EACH LETTERED SQUARE INTO THE MATCHING SQUARE ON THE BLANK GRID. WHEN YOU'VE FINISHED USE ROWDY REDS AND HEAVY PURPLES TO COLOUR MAGNETO IN.

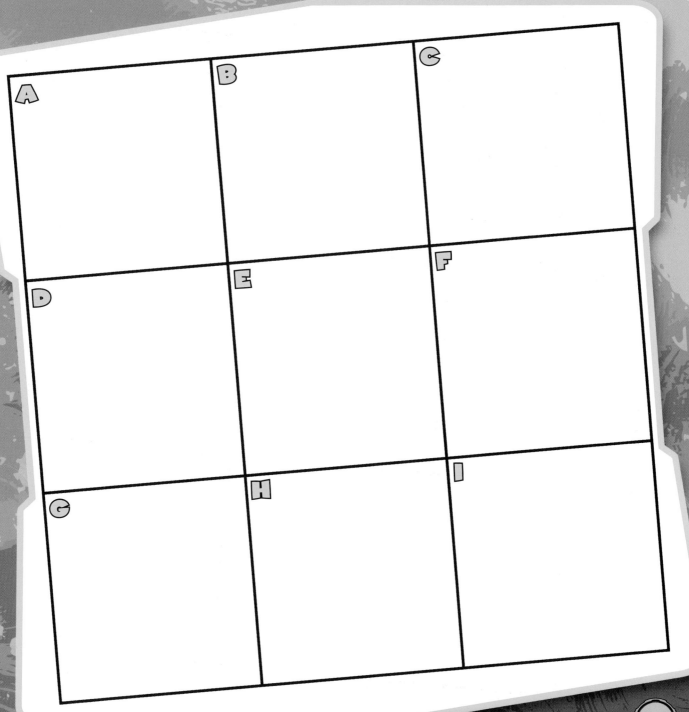

FIRE AND ICE

Do you admire the Silver Surfer's style? YES NO

Do you think Cyclops' laser vision is super-cool? YES NO

Have you ever wanted to go on a skiing holiday? YES NO

Is ice cream your dream dessert? YES

Are you a born risk-taker? YES NO

Are you happiest basking on the beach? YES NO

Are you a big fan of fireworks? YES NO

NEW RECRUITS HUMAN TORCH AND ICEMAN COULDN'T BE MORE DIFFERENT! WHICH HERO IS MOST LIKE YOU? TRACE YOUR FINGER ALONG THE PATHS ON THIS FUN FLOWCHART, ANSWERING THE YES OR NO QUESTIONS. AT THE END YOU'LL DISCOVER WHERE YOUR ALLEGIANCE LIES.

HUMAN TORCH

Do you have a big brother or sister that drives you nuts? **YES** / **NO**

Do you like standing out from the crowd? **YES** / **NO**

Would your friends describe you as hot-headed? **YES** / **NO**

Are you a winter person? **YES** / **NO**

Do you think that you're a natural prankster? **YES** / **NO**

Would you choose cool blues over sizzling scarlets? **YES** / **NO**

Watch out – Human Torch fans can be too hot to handle sometimes! You're a bold personality who always lights up the room.

ICEMAN

You're as cool as a cucumber, just like the Iceman! You're totally laid back... but if someone crossed you you'd freeze them out fast!

107

ANSWERS

PAGE 18: THOR'S WORD CRUSH

```
I R O N M A N
      J E T S
    L O K I
  V I L L A I N V I L L E
M R F A N T A S T I C
    S H I E L D
    F O R C E F I E L D
```

PAGE 20: CALLING ALL SQUADDIES!

1. In the Helicarrier
2. Wolverine
3. 3
4. Spider-Man
5. Reading a Super Hero Squad manual
6. 11

PAGE 32: RUSH AND RESCUE!

C) Silver Surfer

PAGE 33: DR DOOM'S HIT LIST

1. Iron Man / 2. Hulk / 3. Human Torch
4. Hawkeye / 5. Thing

PAGE 36: WHO SAID THAT?

1. D / 2. A / 3. E /
4. F / 5. B / 6. C

PAGES 38-39: LIGHT 'EM UP!

1. DOC OCK
2. MYSTIQUE
3. SENTINEL
4. LOKI
5. MAGNETO
6. SUPER SKRULL
7. DR DOOM
8. ABOMINATION

PAGE 40: DISAPPEARING LETTERS

G	P	D	G	O	H	Z	H	P	K
W	I	V	Q	K	P	B	S	N	X
B	J	F	K	E	X	K	K	S	V
X	J	Y	V	D	Z	U	L	F	H
H	K	C	W	Q	P	A	R	P	W
R	Q	Y	U	R	O	G	L	D	U
Q	L	H	X	H	Y	D	V	Z	V
K	Y	J	X	M	H	F	O	J	B
P	D	P	K	D	Q	D	G	L	K
V	Z	O	H	P	W	J	F	Y	Q

The Super Hero is ICEMAN.

PAGE 41: MORPHING MYSTIQUE

C

PAGES 42-43: OPERATION SQUAD QUAD!

Iron Man: Armour Up! / **Spider-Man:** Webs / **Invisible Woman:** Human Torch / **Wolverine:** Three / **Hulk:** When he's angry / **Nick Fury:** General Ross / **Human Torch:** Flame On'!

PAGE 53: SEARCH THE SENTINELS

The Super Hero is Hawkeye.
There are 14 Sentinels at large.

PAGES 58: HERO HEAD-TO-HEAD

```
      T           C
    T H A W K E Y E
    H O           C
    O R E P T I L       F
    R             O     A
                  P     L
    M R F A N T A S T I C O N
                        N
      D     M Y S T I Q U E S
      O     A             E
      C     G             N
    A B O M I N A T I O N T
      C     E             I
    L O K I T             N
            O             E
                          L
            S
```

PAGE 60: FALCON'S QUICK QUIZ

1. b. Silver Surfer / 2. c. Redwing
3. a. Spider-Man / 4. c. Colossus
5. a. Wolverine / 6. c. Thing
7. c. Hawkeye / 8. a. Thor
9. b. Iceman / 10. b. Iron Man

PAGES 72-73: PUZZLE PATROL

PAGE 74: NICK'S NOTE

I need your help! A devious plot by **DR DOOM** and **MAGNETO** has lured me away from Super Hero **CITY**. Now I'm trapped in the dungeons of **DOOM CASTLE**! **ABOMINATION** is guarding the cell door while the rest of the **VILLAINS** are out causing trouble. Tell **GENERAL ROSS** to raise the alarm in the **HELICARRIER**. He's got to send in **IRON MAN** and the rest of the **HEROES** right away! Over and out, Nick Fury

PAGE 75: WATCH WOLVIE GO!

GOOD	FEARLESS	SPITEFUL	DESPICABLE	SCARY	TREACHEROUS	BOSSY	BITTER
WEEDY	STRONG	EVIL	SHIFTY	ROTTEN	VAIN	UNPLEASANT	FOUL
MEAN	NOBLE	VALIANT	DARING	HORRID	BULLYING	LOATHSOME	WRONG
COWARDLY	DEVIOUS	MONSTROUS	COURAGEOUS	LOYAL	DECENT	HONEST	TYRANNICAL
WEAK	SLY	ANGRY	FIENDISH	CREEPY	FALSE	TOUGH	DEMANDING
NASTY	GREEDY	SHAMELESS	DISHONEST	SELFISH	BAD	BOLD	GALLANT
CRUEL	SNEAKY	ARROGANT	UNDERHAND	VILE	MERCILESS	BIG-HEADED	BRAVE
SCHEMING	CRIMINAL	UNKIND	CALLOUS	WICKED	DECEITFUL	VILLAINOUS	HEROIC

PAGE 78: WHO'S WHO CLUES

1. Spider-Man / 2. Doc Ock
3. Mystique / 4. Iceman

PAGE 82: ODD SQUAD OUT

C

PAGES 84-85: DARING DOZEN WORDSEARCH

I	N	V	I	S	I	B	L	E	W	O	M	A	N
C	T	N	B	R	P	P	K	Z	O	L	M	I	Q
I	I	H	F	J	L	I	D	B	L	D	V	D	W
T	R	X	C	X	D	L	D	S	V	J	A	N	G
S	O	A	Z	R	L	P	R	E	E	K	G	F	Z
A	N	H	P	Z	O	O	K	M	R	Q	S	M	S
T	M	E	C	A	W	T	T	L	I	M	P	G	P
N	A	M	E	C	I	Y	N	K	N	Y	A	Y	O
A	N	P	R	Y	R	K	W	A	E	T	K	N	L
F	S	U	S	S	O	L	O	C	M	F	L	B	C
R	E	P	T	I	L	X	S	F	G	U	U	D	Y
M	O	B	D	Y	E	Y	E	K	W	A	H	E	C

PAGE 86: BAD ANAGRAMS

1. DR DOOM / 2. ABOMINATION
3. SUPER SKRULL / 4. MAGNETO
5. LOKI / 6. MYSTIQUE

PAGE 87: SPIDEY'S SECRETS

1. True / 2. False / 3. True / 4. True
5. False / 6. True / 7. False / 8. True
9. True / 10. False

PAGE 98: PRACTICE MAKES PERFECT!

A. Iron Man

B. Thor

C. Reptil

D. Thing

PAGE 99: SECRET SQUAD

MEET OUTSIDE THE BAXTER BUILDING IN ONE MINUTE!

PAGE 102: THOR TRANSLATOR GAME

1. D / 2. C / 3. H / 4. G / 5. F / 6. B / 7. A / 8. E

PAGE 103: LOKI'S LAIR